ELMAR TRUNZ-CARLISI

TRANSLATED BY GEOFFREY STEINHERZ

Practical
MUSCLE
TRAINING

Targeted Body Building for Men and Women

BARNES
& NOBLE
BOOKS

NEW YORK

Contents
Practical Muscle Training

Foreword

Muscle Training is a professional treatment of the subject that is aimed for anyone who wants to systematically improve their build, posture, health, and performance. In muscle training, very minor differences determine failure or success; the right and the wrong amount of weights are never far apart. "Practical Muscle Training" will allow you to train with the help of the latest scientific knowledge.

The introductory section, entitled "Safe and Effective Training" starting on page 7, explains the practical basis for training and offers basic training plans. The extensive practical section entitled "The Exercises" starting on page 37, explains all of the most important exercises currently practiced in modern fitness studios and in the home. There are precise and easy-to-follow descriptions of the basic exercises and their variations. Detailed anatomical illustrations clearly show the workings of each of the main and supporting muscles.

Armed with this knowledge, you can build up your muscles in a targeted fashion and significantly improve the quality of your strength training at all levels.

Elmar Trunz-Carlisi

Safe and Effective
Training

Are you demanding, especially when it comes to your body, your figure, and your physical performance? Then you are probably looking for the most effective exercises and and optimal training quality. This chapter provides you with precise information and practical tips you can put into effect immediately in order to reach your training goal quickly, without undesirable side effects. You will learn how to correctly combine the individual exercises and how to systematically set up your training program.

Successful
from the Beginning

How do you gauge yourself?

Start racking up successes on the first day by picking realistic goals and the right individual starting point. Efficient muscle training can be planned. In the first instance it's a question of having a system. If you can create the right mix of training and choice of exercise, and stick to your chosen program, you'll be able to do it. Depending on the type of training you want to do, you need to consider a few important points to make sure you get it right.

Beginners

Never used a systematic muscle training program? No problem! In fact, quite the contrary, this means you have the greatest potential for improvement. You are starting more or less from scratch and will appreciate success when it comes. For fast results and to avoid undesirable side-effects, you need to stick to a few important rules of the game. Cartilage, ligaments, and tendons need an especially long warm-up phase, so they can withstand the stress that they will usually be placed under from training. So stay relaxed during the early weeks, and feel your way slowly. When selecting exercises, favor simple and easy-to-master movements. In this way, you'll be able to rapidly achieve a solid basis in order to then build up your muscles.

Second-timers

The longer the break you have taken from regular training, the further away you are from your peak form. Good condition can be maintained for a while, but in the long run, muscle tension and mass are lost. As a general rule, if you haven't trained for three years or longer you should behave as though you were starting from scratch. This means that the initial performance potential will have to be built up slowly and patiently, just as if you were a beginner. Don't kid yourself into overdoing it due to false pride, hold yourself back consciously during the first weeks of training. The guideline that guarantees success in the initial phase is "easy does it." If you have a lot of experience with movement and good coordination, you can select exercises that are technically demanding. What makes the difference in the beginning is keeping the amount of exercise you do at a reasonable level.

Experienced athletes

The more experienced you are and the more ambitious your training goals, the faster you will reach your limit. That is not to say, by any means, that competition-oriented athletes should be constantly extending their limits. By systematically changing the exercises and making targeted use of exercise variations, you will give your muscles the necessary stimulation that will enable them to do more and lift heavier weights. That way, you avoid monotony, while addressing the various functions of your muscles evenly, and at the same time reducing the risk of strain. The exercise section of this book contains a wide range of exercises and variations that will enable you to work on all the major muscle groups from legs to shoulders. Use them in a targeted fashion to work out a complete routine.

Success for every fitness level

"No pain—no gain". This slogan has had its day in the fitness world. New scientific studies prove that training to exhaustion is quite unnecessary for most people, even professional athletes. In fact, research conducted by sports scientist Wolfgang Buskies, who is based in Bayreuth, Germany, shows that it is possible to achieve a great deal from only an eight-week training program, meaning that much can be achieved in a relatively short time. This opens up the prospect of effective strength training for almost all of the target groups while keeping exercise enjoyable and pain-free.

What level of intensity?

A simple and effective method to find out how intensively you should train is determining your level of stress tolerance. It is the way to sense your own level of exertion and assign it an intensity scale. You will find the appropriate training weight by systematic trial and error. The standard of assessment is always the last repetition that was performed without error. In this way, the training always fits the level of performance. If, for instance, the weight in several sessions is more manageable than anticipated, it can be increased. Conversely, you will react to changes in the type of training when the intensity is suddenly reduced. The standard maximum strength tests still in use are relatively less practical in comparison, and are very exacting and time-consuming, since each machine needs to be tested individually.

The intensity scale

1 = Very easy: You feel the weight, but only barely.
2 = Somewhat difficult: You feel a strain, but you still have a large reserve of strength.
3 = Moderately difficult: The exercise program ends before you are exhausted, and you can even add a few more repetitions.

4 = Difficult: You are almost exhausted when you finish, and can only manage a few more reps.
5 = Very difficult: You are exhausted by the time you finish.

PICKING THE RIGHT LEVEL

➤ **Beginners and second-timers** should choose a degree of exertion that they consider to lie between 1 and 2, corresponding to "very easy" and "somewhat difficult". The series of exercises should always end well before the point of exhaustion. As your level of fitness increases, you should consider increasing the level to moderately difficult (3).
➤ **Experienced athletes** can master—depending on training status and goal—moderately difficult (3), difficult (4) and even very difficult (5) exercises, if they have the appropriate constitution.
➤ **Performance-oriented athletes:** As long as there are no health reasons not to do so, performance-oriented athletes can perform the exercises each time to the point of exhaustion (5).

Whether beginner or pro, picking the right training level is crucial to success.

Creating the
Right Training Program

Repetition numbers and muscle contraction duration

The numbers of times a given exercise is repeated is only a reliable guide to the right training if the duration of muscle tension (the amount of time during which the muscles are contracted) is defined. For instance, twenty short, sharp movements will have a shorter muscle contraction time than eight slow repetitions. Where fitness is concerned, the so-called controlled dynamic tempo has proven itself. Movements are performed smoothly and at a regular pace, which is easy to monitor at all times.

Focus is determined by the training phase

There are around three training phases: adaptation, buildup, and stabilization. For all of them, many repetitions of each exercise are recommended.

➤ **Strength and endurance training during the adaptation phase:** The recommended number of reps is 15 through 25. Gradually reduce the number while increasing the amount of weight you use.

➤ **Maximum strength training in the buildup phase:** During this phase you slowly increase the level of intensity. The series of exercises starts at 10 to 15, and is subsequently reduced to 8 to 12 repetitions with correspondingly heavier weights. For intermuscular coordination (Interplay of the Muscles, page 32) training, few repetitions (1 to 3) are required in order to achieve maximum intensity.

➤ **Maintaining strength in the stabilization phase:** In order to maintain the level of strength that has been gained, 10 to 12 repetitions in a two to three times a week training routine should be enough. If there is insufficient time, train with 8 to 12 repetitions, keeping the weight lifted as high as possible. The rule is, the shorter the time available, the more intensive the training.

The different phases of movement

If you train as recommended, using a controlled dynamic tempo, you will be placing demands on all the possible movements of the muscles (see info box). This works in the following way: Lift the weight in one to two seconds, depending on the length of the movement (**concentric phase**). Now, guide the weight with the same speed of movement, i.e. one to two seconds, back to the starting position (**eccentric phase**). To ensure that the transition proceeds smoothly and in a controlled manner, the weight can be briefly held at the return point (**static phase**). During individual repetitions the weight is not

---

➤ **Info** Muscle operating modes

➤ Our muscles have different capabilities: They can overcome resistance (lift a weight), work against it (move back the weight in a controlled way) or keep it steady (maintain the weight in one position).

➤ If a weight is lifted and moved, the muscles are shortened or contracted. This is called dynamic concentric contraction. When the weight is lowered, the contracted muscle is stretched at high muscle tension (dynamic-excentric contraction), until there is a return to the starting position. At the return point of the movement, if the weight is briefly held in one position, the muscle is working statically, i.e., with constant muscle length while at the same time muscle tension is maintained. This mode is also called isometric contraction.

➤ The muscles react differently, depending on the phase of movement and the execution. In muscle training, the various capabilities of the muscles can be combined or individually addressed.

Short, intensive training sessions will maintain your strength at the right level

Systematic elbow tensor training will provide a hefty boost to your tennis serve.

released, in order to keep the muscle continuously under tension. One cycle of movement, depending on the path of movement of the machine or the exercise, lasts for around two to four seconds.

The eccentric phase is especially important

Unfortunately, the eccentric phase, when the weight is returned the starting position, is often performed too quickly and is unfocused, reducing the beneficial effects of training. This also introduces the danger of the weight falling out of control back into the joint causing it to be swung up again, in an uncontrolled movement. Since the muscle in the eccentric phase can develop a lot of strength, it makes sense as a variation for advanced training to concentrate on the braking phase of the movement and to extend it correspondingly by about three to four seconds.

Dynamic exercises take priority over static ones

In fitness-oriented strength training, dynamic demands should have priority. As a rule, if these exercises are performed correctly, they put less strain on the joints as well as on the cardiovascular system. In contrast with static exercises, increased joint strain can occur when pressure is localized on a joint held in a certain position. This may also produce a steep rise in blood pressure, especially if mistakes are made in the breathing technique (page 23). As a supplement to a complex training program, static holding exercises make a lot of sense. Some muscle groups can be especially well addressed in this way. This is true, for instance, for the transverse stomach musculature (*Transversus abdominis*), which is extremely helpful for posture control (Exercise on page 90).

Strength training as training for other types of sport

Whether their sport is tennis, golf, or football, almost all athletes perform special supplementary strength exercises as training for their sport. On the one hand, they benefit from targeted strengthening of the muscles that are called upon to perform. On the other hand, selected exercises ensure that the muscles that are less in demand for their chosen sport receive their share of exercise so that muscle imbalance is avoided or compensated for (See the table on page 168). With compensatory training, the goal is an overall harmony and uniformity in muscle development. It is especially important to symmetrically strengthen the trunk muscles. Exercises which mimic the movement sequences of the particular sport and allow for safe training at high intensity are best suited to increase performance. This enables a high maximum strength to be achieved, and will also improve endurance when the sport is being played.

THE EXAMPLE OF TENNIS

It makes sense for a tennis player to train for maximum strength of the elbow extensor, in order to give a boost to the serve. Strengthening the trunk muscles and the thigh extensor supports the dynamic of the sequence of movements used when serving. Even endurance and sharp, sudden movements can be simulated by using strength training machines under ideal conditions. This requires very good movement control. Geared cable weight-lifting machines are especially well suited for this purpose, because the weight block only moves a little in proportion to the movement and does not "fly away" during acceleration and have to be caught again at the expense of increased strain on the joints. In order to increase the power of service, in addition to maximum strength training, tennis players can use a geared cable weight-lifting machine to perform the maximum elbow stretch, which will help them avoid "tennis elbow."

Types of training, frequency, and duration

In order to achieve the desired training effect, the phases of muscle tension and recovery must be in the right proportion to each other. In practice, multi-set and circuit training as well as single-set training, are used.

Multi-set and circuit training

➤ **Multi-set training** consists of an exercise conducted several times in succession with a pause in between before moving on to the next exercise. For example, between a series with twelve repetitions, breaks of up to three minutes have to be taken. In this way one muscle after another is brought to the point of exhaustion.

➤ **Circuit training** consists of exercises performed consecutively, without taking a break in between. The sequence of the exercises should be chosen in order to ensure that muscle groups that are as far apart as possible are exercised in turn, because the normal breaks are not taken. In this way, several circuits can follow each other in quick succession, but a break should be taken at the end of each circuit.

ADVANTAGES AND DISADVANTAGES

The advantage of circuit training is mainly one of time-saving. Its constantly changing demands make this approach the most motivating for many people. In contrast, with multi-set training, the muscles can be trained in a more concentrated fashion, which is why it is preferred by most dedicated athletes.

The various training phases and goals can be adapted to both types of training routine. The more emphasis there is on building up muscle and the higher the training intensity, the more likely it is that multi-set training will be appropriate. For enhancing general fitness, circuit training is generally perfectly adequate.

Athletes who want to train their muscles to peak performance often prefer the more demanding multiple-set training.

Single-set training on the rise

Single-set training is a sort of compromise between multi-set and circuit training. Recent studies indicate that this kind of training is very time-saving. The exercises are performed in sequence one after the other. In contrast to circuit training, the muscle should be trained to exhaustion within a series of exercises performed at each station, while with circuit training several series of exercises are performed in sequence. With single-set training, the number of repetitions and the amount of weight are precisely correlated. The weight is selected in such a way that twelve cleanly executed movements can be performed with maximum effort. In this way, it is possible to achieve the maximum effect from training in a relative short amount of time. Because of the high intensity, single-set training is generally better suited for more advanced individuals.

How often should you train?

Even when you have found the type of training that is right for you, the questions of frequency and duration remain. Strength training is best organized during the week so that between the training sessions there is a break of one to two days for the relevant muscle groups. Any-one wanting to train more frequently or even daily should divide the training routine so that on one day, for instance, the upper body is trained and on the next day, the legs are trained. When training for fitness, two to three training sessions per week have proven optimal, with the sessions distributed as evenly as possible over the week, but they should not follow each other on consecutive days. When training less often, a regular schedule should be maintained and training performed with that much more concentration.

How long should you train for?

The length of training is determined by personal training goals for the time available. You should allow at least 30 minutes for strength-training. But always bear in mind that even if the training sessions are short, the warm-up and cooling down phases should not be neglected. A period of 60 minutes is optimal, but training can certainly be extended to 90 minutes. In any case, it is always better to train for a short period with greater concentration than for a longer period less rigorously.

➤ Info A sensible training program

	Adjustment phase (around 1–2 months)	Build-up phase (at least 6 months)	Stabilization phase (no limit)
Level of intensity	very easy (1)* somewhat difficult (2)	moderately difficult (3) difficult (4) very difficult (5)**	moderate (4) to difficult (3) very difficult (5)**
Number of repetitions	20–25 15–20	10–15 8–12	10–15 / 8–12
Type of training	circuit training preferred	Multi-set training preferred	Single-set training preferred
	* The numbers from 1 to 5 refer to the intensity scale on page 9	** Only recommended for performance-oriented athletes	

Training muscles correctly

Sore muscles? Poor training!

Muscle soreness is the result of tiny wounds in the interior of the muscle cells. It is not the result of muscle hyperacidity as was once thought. When the muscle begins to ache it is by no means acidic! The micro-wounds occur especially from unaccustomed and abrupt (eccentric) movements. Muscle soreness is therefore by no means a precondition for muscle buildup, as it still says in some books about fitness. On the contrary, people experiencing severe muscle soreness should stop training because the pain will merely impede their progress.

FIRST AID MEASURES

When strength training is performed correctly, there is seldom any muscle soreness. If it happens, it is not a serious problem as a rule. The symptoms normally subside by themselves after a couple of days. In this phase, however, the muscles should only be lightly exercised. Easy movements and the application of heat encourage the circulation and hasten the healing process. If the soreness does not disappear after five days, you should consult a doctor and find out the reason for the problem.

Always stretch well!

To enable the muscle to develop full performance potential, its stretching capacity has to be developed or maintained. With a program that relies exclusively on strength training, loss of movement can occur if countermeasures are not taken at the right time. It therefore makes sense to integrate light stretching exercises into the program. These can be done as warm-up (page 30) and cooling-down (Page 35) exercises. In separate training sessions, outside of strength training, you can perform longer and more intensive stretching without reducing the strengthening effect (see the literature on this subject under stretching on page 163).

STRETCHING AND STRENGTH TRAINING

For stretching during strength training, light rocking motions are appropriate (no overstretching!). Recent studies show that static (sustained) stretching has the possible disadvantage of overstretching the muscles and therefore making them less responsive to strength training. Prolonged stretching exercises after the training can impede regeneration, which is of primary importance for the fitness athlete. Light stretching during the breaks actively supports recovery.

➤ Tip   The right stretching technique

Depending on the goal—general improvement or maintenance of general mobility—different stretching techniques are recommended.

➤ If you want to **improve your mobility,** then perform the stretch exercises on a daily basis at home. Sustained stretching is especially good for this, in that you slowly assume the stretching position, and hold it over three to four (or more) breathing cycles. By exhalation, the stretching can be slightly increase each time, without becoming painful.

➤ **In order to maintain mobility** you should integrate stretch exercises in your warm-up and cooling-off exercises. During a warm-up, the muscles and joints are gently broken in. Stretching at this time ensures that residual contraction (temporary mobility impairments) or as a consequence of the training can be immediately corrected again. As a stretching technique, light bouncing movements are recommended: You assume a simple stretching position and increase the stretching by repeated, controlled bouncing. Use this technique especially carefully, however.

If muscle soreness strikes again, gentle massage will stimulate circulation in the tissue.

Stretch exercises for all body areas should always accompany training. In this way the muscles can reach full performance potential.

Strength training before endurance?

In fitness studios and gyms, strength- and endurance-training are often combined. If you are concerned with improving your overall fitness, that makes sense. However, the sequence of the training focal points has to be adjusted to the training goals and individual circumstances. If strength training is your primary concern, then —after a thorough warm-up—you should start with this part of the program. This has the advantage of preparing and relaxing the muscles so they can then take their maximum strain. Conversely, you are recommended to start with cardio-training (endurance training), if your focus is to improve your endurance. This sequence really makes sense when you are trying to metabolize fat, that is if you want to increase the fat-burning part of total energy consumption (for instance, instead of 40 percent, you want 60 percent of available energy to be produced from fat). If you perform strength-training before endurance-training, then the muscles will become hyperacidic over time, which impedes the fat-burning in this phase.

THE RIGHT SEQUENCE

When and which sequence you pick depends on your current training status. If you have been inactive for a long period of time and you just want to increase your general level of fitness, you should do as much cardio-training as possible in the first few weeks. This will better prepare your body for the strain of strength-training. In addition, without previous strain from strength-training, cardio-training will "teach" your metabolism to use more fat as an energy source. These considerations also apply for anyone who wants to lose weight. Advanced athletes who are primarily concerned with buildup of muscle should put strength training in the mid-point and start with this part of the program. Depending on the extent and length of training and the available time a separation of strength and endurance training is recommended, so that each is performed on different days of the week.

Always warm up first, for instance on the bicycle ergometer.

Your Personal
Training Program

Setting up a training session

What should your personal training program look like in detail? A couple of primary criteria are provided here as guidance. Our stabilization test on page 30 will give you additional help.

A couple of basic rules

➤ Train the **flexor muscles before the extensors**, the biceps (flexor) before the triceps (extensor). The reason is that the bending, or flexor, muscles are generally weaker, and this way you open up the way for the extensor training (active stretching).

➤ **Complex exercises** (such as rowing, see the rowing machines, page 98) should precede isolated movements (such as the Butterfly Reverse, page 124). This has the advantage of using individual muscles that are already pre-activated and that can then be further loaded in a precise and targeted way. If this is not done, a "smaller" muscle that may already be tired can disrupt the interaction of the muscle chain when brought into play in complex training and thereby deflect the movement.

➤ Make sure that the muscles responsible for **posture control** do not become prematurely fatigued, so that a safe body posture is maintained until the end of the training session. For this reason, you should not start the session with the strenuous trunk muscle exercises, but rather with the limbs.

➤ Save your **favorite exercises** and most strenuous exercises for the end of the session, beginning by exercising the weaker muscles. This avoids the danger of aggravating existing imbalances over time.

➤ It is up to you whether you begin with the legs or the arms. The most important thing is to find a **system** and to stick to it as closely as possible. In a health club or gym situation this is not always possible, due to the fact that the machine you need may not be immediately available. If this happens, you can alter the program sequence slightly or just move on to similar machines or exercises. The more exercises you master, the more flexible your body will be.

The three phases of training

Study the overall system of a training session when setting up your training program.

➤ You should start with a five- to ten-minute **warm-up** (see Warm-up, page 30), to prepare the muscles for the strain they will take. The warm-up should also include special stretching exercises.

➤ Then there is the main muscle-training part of the program, which in the context of complex fitness training can also be combined with an endurance section (page 15).

➤ Training should end with a **cooling-down phase** (page 35), which should include the first set of warm-ups but in reverse order.

Framework for training plans

On the following pages, you will find three training programs to choose from which you can mix and match as you please. The examples feature different focal points depending on training type. In order to provide a better overview, eight sets of exercises are shown, which are dedicated to exercising a particular area or muscle. The training plans vary, depending on individual needs. The left-hand column features exercises for beginners, in the center there are the advanced exercises and on the right are those for experienced gymnasts and athletes. Each section has a page reference to the detailed description in the exercise section. You find this underneath. With more training experience the level of intensity and the number of training sessions are increased in groups or sets, while the number of repetitions is reduced.

Use the three model framework plans in order to design and vary your individual training plan.

Back and stomach

This program concentrates on the muscle groups that are especially important for the maintenance of health and stabilization of the spinal column. It is suitable for all target groups, from beginners to athletes, in order to prevent back problems or to counteract them. The goal is a stable, symmetrically developed trunk muscle structure which protectively surrounds the back and guards it against in-

correct loading. The program is so arranged to switch back and forth between groups of muscles, in order to distribute the impact evenly. It is important to train in an absolutely pain-free condition. If, in spite of using the correct movement technique, back problems arise, omit this exercise for the time being.

Muscle area	Beginners		Advanced		Athletes	
	Exercise	Page	Exercise	Page	Exercise	Page
Rectus abdominis	Abdominal bench	p. 80	Seated abdom., trainer	p. 74	Reverse abdominal trainer	p. 82
Upper back and and shoulder muscles	Lever seated row	p. 98	Lateral pull-down	p. 94	Front pull-down	p. 96
Oblique Rectus abdominis	Twisted crunch	p. 88	Twisted crunch	p. 88	Diagonal crunch	p. 89
Lower back muscles	Lever back extension	p. 92	Lumbar trainer	p. 104	Lever back extension	p. 92
Lateral abdominal muscles	Lever side-bend	p. 84	Side bending with cable	p. 78	Cable side-bend	p. 78
Upper back and shoulder muscles	Lateral pull-down	p. 94	Reverse butterfly	p. 124	Diagonal lateral cable raise	p. 132
Lower back muscles	Backward leg lift with bench	p. 106	Lever back extension	p. 92	Lumbar trainer	p. 104
Rectus abdominis	Ab-roller	p. 86	Abdominal bench	p. 80	Cable crunch	p. 76

Amount*

Level of intensity	moderately difficult (3)		difficult (4)		very difficult (5)	
Numbers of repetitions	10–15		8–12		8–12	
Runs/Sets	2		2–4		3–5	

* All numbers refer to the muscle build-up phase of the training (page 10)

All types of crunches strengthen the abdominals.
It is important to perform the movement without swinging!

Stomach, legs, and buttocks

If you want to shape the lower body, this is the right program for you. The exercises cover all the important muscle groups in the calves, thighs, hips, and buttocks. In addition, there are exercises for the oblique and lateral abdominals, which mainly help shape the waist.

Muscle region	Beginner		Advanced		Athlete	
	Exercise	Page	Exercise	Page	Exercise	Page
Leg flexor	Seated leg curl	p. 44	Seated leg curl	p. 44	Leg curler lying on the stomach	p. 52
Leg extensor	Seated leg press	p. 40	Barbell squat	p. 48	Barbell squat	p. 48
Abductors	Lever seated hip abductor	p. 56	Lever seated hip abductor	p. 56	Cable hip abductor	p. 62
Adductor	Lever seated hip adductor	p. 58	Cable hip adductor	p. 64	Lever seated hip adductor	p. 58
Buttocks muscles	Lever kneeling hip extension	p. 60	Reverse leg lift with cable	p. 68	Hip extender with cable	p. 66
Oblique abdominals	Twisted crunch	p. 88	Twisted crunch	p. 88	Diagonal crunch	p. 89
Calf muscles	Seated calf press	p. 46	Calf lift with dumbbells	p. 50	Calf lift with dumbbells	p. 50
Lateral abdominals	Ab-roller	p. 86	Abdominal bench	p. 80	Reverse abdominal trainer	p. 82

Amount						
Level of intensity	moderately difficult (3)		difficult (4)		very difficult (5)	
Repetition numbers	10–15		8–12		8–12	
Runs/Sets	ca. 2		2–4		3–5	

A classic exercise for developing the chest muscles: the push-up.

Chest, shoulders, and arms

This program is generally designed to build up a trained and athletic upper body. It combines exercises around the shoulder area and supplements them with a strengthening of the arm muscles. Special exercises for the shoulder-neck area also come into play here.

Muscle region	Beginner		Advanced		Athlete	
	Exercise	Page	Exercise	Page	Exercise	Page
Chest muscles	Lever inclined chest press	p. 108	Bench press with barbell	p. 112	Bench press with barbell	p. 112
Front/upper shoulder muscles	Lever shoulder press	p. 120	Neck press with dumbbells	p. 126	Lateral raise with dumbbells	p. 128
Chest muscles	Butterfly	p. 110	Butterfly	p. 110	Cable standing fly	p. 116
Back shoulder muscles	Shoulder raise lying on the stomach	p. 138	Reverse butterfly	p. 124	Reverse fly with dumbbells	p. 130
Biceps	Lever preacher curl	p. 140	Biceps curl with barbell	p. 146	Concentration curl	p. 154
Shoulder and neck muscles	Upright cable row	p. 134	Upright cable row	p. 134	Upright cable row	p. 134
Triceps	Lever triceps extension	p. 142	Assisted pull-up	p. 122	Dumbbell kickback	p. 156
Forearm	Barbell reverse wrist curl	p. 152	Barbell reverse wrist curl	p. 152	Barbell reverse wrist curl	p. 152

Amount						
Level of intensity	moderately difficult (3)		difficult (4)		very difficult (5)	
Repetition numbers	10–15		8–12		8–12	
Runs/Sets	ca. 2		2–4		3–5	

Training
correctly

Movement technique

A good machine can be adjusted to the size and proportions of your body. This means that the machine must be capable of adjustment in order for you to be able to do the exercise in the correct, joint-protecting position. With high-quality machines, this is accomplished quickly and comfortably with a flick of the wrist. The following approach should serve as orientation.

Optimum adjustment for strength machines

➤ **Axis adjustment:** Check first that the axes of the joints of your body correspond to the axis of the machine. For example, on the leg-stretching machine (page 42) the thigh must be positioned so that the point of rotation of the knee joint lies in a horizontal extension of the rotation joint of the machine. This adjustment procedure is not so simple and an experienced trainer should help you. The better the correspondence between joint and machine, the less the danger of strain on the joints. This can lead to scissors strain, which is especially dangerous for cartilage. If you train with heavy weights you should select a position very carefully, because with an increase in weight, faulty loading could pay you back with interest.

➤ **Seat height:** Since with strength machines, training is primarily performed in a sitting position, the correct height adjustment of the seat is crucial. The following is important to remember: Adjust the seat so that the knees are bent approximately at right angles. A knee joint angle of about 80 degrees is optimal (The reference point for all angles is the vertical at zero degrees, page 38). This angle creates a good pelvic position, which in turn supports an erect posture with natural movement in the spine. A wider angle will cause you to hunch your back while a narrower angle leads to a arched back in the lumbar area.

➤ **Padding:** When the axis adjustment is right, the padded areas should be shaped around this position. With the leg extender (page 42), this means that the distance of the seat back should be adjusted, so that the entire back is flush against the padding and is supported by it.

➤ **Handles:** In addition it makes sense to use the handles, if the machine has them. A measured pull of the arms provides additional stability and helps to keep the upper body erect.

Stabilizing the whole body

When the machine is correctly adjusted, you can start. The exercise always begins with a directed tensing of the trunk muscles in order to stabilize the body. The actual movement proceeds from this controlled starting position, supported by the stabilizing muscles. This produces a dual benefit: You avoid undesirable side-effects and compensation in the adjacent joints and you deploy more muscle groups which, in turn, improves the economy of training. People who train intelligently do not merely focus on one area at the expense of others, but maintain an overview of the body as an integrated whole, paying attention to support muscles that enable movement.

SEATED

➤ **To tense the muscles:** Tense the large muscle chain (buttocks, back, stomach) in order to actively stabilize the starting position. You can do this by means of the following trick: Put pressure on your heels by imagining you want to push them forward. Your posture will automatically become erect.

➤ **Foot position:** Keep the position erect with a slightly straddled foot position, that is clearly more than the width of your hips. Many modern machines have a padded saddle, which allows for such a straddled position. Wide, non-ergonomic seats make this kind of body stabilization more difficult.

STANDING

It is even more important for the body to be stable when using dumbbells or when cable training from a standing position. There are also a few tips here which help create an optimal position.

➤ **Foot position:** Place the feet in a parallel and stable position at more than hips width. The feet should be turned slightly outward. With some exercises, for instance with swinging movements with the cable machine for chest muscle training (page 116), a slight stride position can be assumed.

➤ **Knee joints:** The knees should be somewhat bent. That creates a stronger activation of the leg muscles, along with a slight raising of the pelvis. In that way you counteract an arched back.

➤ **Upper body:** Lean the upper body—depending on the exercise—forward slightly and "push" the breastbone consciously forward. This straightens out the upper body and the back regains its natural posture with a slightly concave sway in the lumbar spine.

The individual range of movement

In training you should use your individual range of movement to optimum advantage. That means, of course, that the machine must allow for a certain amount of play. In professional jargon, a distinction is made between anatomical and physiological ranges of movement.

➤ The **anatomical range of movement** (amplitude) shows the maximum extent of movement up to the "locking" of the relevant joint.

➤ The **physiological range of movement** (amplitude) describes the range that is possible for you under a convenient loading of the joints.

In training, it is naturally the physiological joint amplitude that is decisive and terminal movements, that is, movements that lead to joint locking, should be avoided at all costs, especially when you add weight or even worse, where there is a swinging movement.

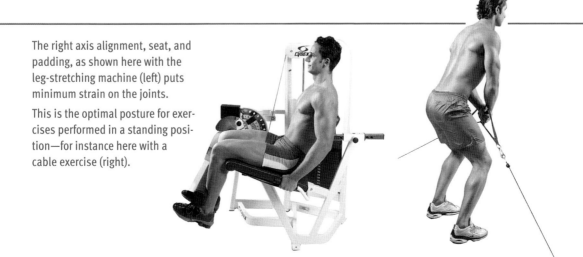

The right axis alignment, seat, and padding, as shown here with the leg-stretching machine (left) puts minimum strain on the joints.

This is the optimal posture for exercises performed in a standing position—for instance here with a cable exercise (right).

THE OPTIMUM RANGE OF MOVEMENT

The optimum range of movement has been exceeded when compensatory movements in the joints or neighboring regions set in. For instance, when you are extending the leg while using a cable machine and the hip buckles outward, the limit of joint movement has been reached or may already have been exceeded. Reduce the extent of the movement by a few degrees and try and find the best limit for you. The same goes for compensation in exercises that may affect the back.

In the case of certain machines, there is a danger that the optimum range of movement may be exceeded at the beginning of the movement. This is especially true for the butterfly (page 110) or the adductor machines (page 58), where each muscle contracts from a pre-stretched position. In order to prevent such excessive strain from the beginning, the best machines of this type are fitted with an entry support.

ANGLE LIMITER AND ENTRY SUPPORT

For this reason, some machines are equipped with an angle limiter, which limits the individual range of action and thereby makes the movement safer. That way, the machine prevents the optimal range of movement from being exceeded, which for beginners and anyone who has inadequate control over movement, as well as for patients in rehabilitation who have a limited range of movement, can be very helpful. Experienced athletes are usually conscious enough of their range of movement not to require this kind of assistance from the machine.

The natural curve of the spine

When the back muscles are involved in training, it is important to take into consideration the natural curve of the spine. This means that in the lumbar spinal region, any so-called lumbar lordosis in the starting or ending position—depending on the exercise—is maintained. Current bio-mechanical research confirms that this precaution will produce especially effective training.

This position is not to be confused with a hollow back, in which the curvature is clearly excessive (the so-called "Grecian bend"). An excessively arched back puts too much strain on the sensitive intervertebral disks. Never strain your back by lifting weights while bent backwards.

In back training, the range of movement is prescribed by the natural, slight curve in the lumbar region.

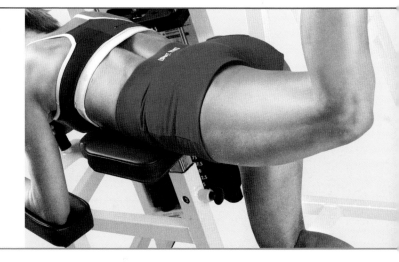

Breathing technique

Anyone who has trained in a health club or gym will be familiar with this picture: cheeks puffed out, mouth clamped shut, a beet-red complexion, and bulging veins in the forehead and neck—a typical case of compressed breathing under intense pressure.

During breathing compression, the air is held in under the strain of lifting. This closes the glottis in the larynx and air is trapped in the stomach cavity and squeezed. This inner pressure is initially produced by tension of the abdominals. Since the abdominals, in addition to a con-

nective tissue-like muscle sheath *(fascia)* are connected to the back extensors, the compression produces a sheath-like surround of the spine, which protects it. Compressed breathing during extreme exertion, for instance when lifting heavy weights, therefore makes good sense, since the disks can be relieved from strain by up to 50 percent. This pressure mechanism should, however, only be used rarely if at all, because holding the breath can substantially raise blood pressure, and thereby put a strain on the heart.

BREATHING RHYTHM AND MOVEMENT

In strength training, regular breathing is very important. The rate of breathing should guide the movement as a rule—not the other way around. As a rule of thumb, exhalation should take place to collapse the most strenuous phase of the exercise, especially when lifting a weight. The exhalation phase runs parallel to bringing down the weight or alternatively, parallel to the return and to the starting position.

➤ **Tip:** In order to practice correct breathing, exhale clearly during the most strenuous phase and emphasize this breathing sequence.

When lifting heavy amounts, compressed breathing can sometimes make sense. In other situations, the free flow of breath is preferable.

Which exercises are best for you

You have the choice between different exercise types: strength machines, dumbbells, cable machines, training benches, and even training without machines, i.e., with just your own body weight. Which approach best suits your goals? The immediate answer is, the more varied the way in which you build up your training over time, the more effective your training will be. The muscles are constantly seeking new stimulation in order to readapt themselves. For this reason, in the exercise section of the book that concentrates on each muscle area you will find the best exercises to be performed on machines, dumbbells, cable equipment, and training benches as well as special gymnastic exercises which you can perform to supplement your machine training.

Strength machines

A significant advantage of the machines is that the movements can be partially performed, thereby reducing the risk of injury or strain. The coordination requirements are less than those that are needed for dumbbell or cable exercises and you can concentrate entirely on the movement. The body is maintained in the correct position and stabilized in the starting position, which also makes it possible to train with heavy weights. Precisely graduated resistance allows for a controlled adaptation to the current performance level. This makes the training more comfortable and easier, especially for the beginner. It does not mean that incorrect movement can be ruled out entirely, however. Even when you are assisted by the most modern technology, it is up to you to train efficiently and protect yourself from injury.

MACHINE TRAINING SUPPLEMENTS THAT MAKE SENSE

In spite of all the advantages of machine training, machines, too, have their limitations. That is because they do not promote optimal coordination, interaction, and the internal activation of the muscles. In this respect, the great advantages of machines in ensuring correct direction and securing the path of movement become a disadvantage. For this reason, as your training experience increases, you are advised to combine machine training with exercises using free weights, as well as cable exercises and those performed with merely the body weight itself.

Training with strength machines (left) —especially for beginners—represents a somewhat reduced risk of injury than training with free weights.

Free weights

The reason dumbbells are used less frequently today than in the past has nothing to do with the way they work, but with the changed parameters of training. Like athletes trained to the peak of fitness, more and more beginners are learning the advantages of strength training on a machine. For beginners, in particular, training with free weights is more difficult and requires close supervision. Weights that are incorrectly installed can slip or contribute to compensatory movements, which, in the worst case, can lead to injury. Systematic learning with the assistance of a trainer is therefore that much more important. A mirror is also useful for checking the movement.

SPECIAL TRAINING EFFECTS

In the long run, dumbbells should become part of every good training program. The value of dumbbell training can be shown clearly by means of a simple example: Say you train on a bench press machine with a starting weight of 80 lbs. After a few months, you will be performing your exercise routine with a weight of 120 lbs—a 50 percent increase. Now try and lie down under a dumbbell stand (with a trainer present), that is also loaded with 120 lbs. You will probably not be able to lift this weight because the training effect gained from the machine can only be partially transferred to a different situation. The same muscle fibers are always addressed with the machine, while the dumbbell calls upon many muscle fibers, in order to counterbalance the weight and move it in a controlled fashion. A similar situation occurs if you want to transfer your performance in strength training to other sports. Here again, there are special conditions for which strength training cannot fully prepare you.

Cable machines

Similar principles apply to cable exercises. As with weights, the body itself must stabilize and balance out the movement. While dumbbell training is mostly for the upper body muscles, cable exercises create possibilities for exercising muscles in the leg, hips, and buttocks. A multitude of special grips and leg sheaths provide a broad palette of exercises for the entire body.

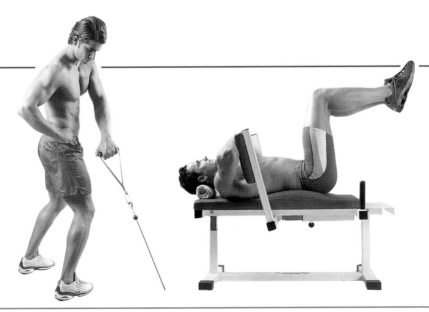

With cable training (left) good self-stabilization is indispensable. Training benches (right) help to increase the gymnastic effect.

WORTH LOOKING AT

➤ **The graduated weight adjustments** on the cable exercise machines are important in order to enable training to proceed in small steps. Otherwise, strain can occur, especially in the hand and elbow joints which training the upper body calls into play.

For the same reason, training should be designed in such a way that with continual change (arms and legs) there are always relaxation phases.

➤ In exercises performed from an upright, standing position **a stable starting position** is essential. For instance, for an abductor pull using the cable machine (page 64), the body must balance out the entire weight standing on one leg while the other leg moves against the resistance of the cable. It is all the more important to begin the training under systematic supervision and with small weights. Otherwise there is a danger that the benefits of training will be nullified by compensatory movements or strained muscles.

Training benches

In comparison with the machines they look rather unassuming, but in terms of training effectiveness they are almost as good. The combination of machine types has proven to be very efficient in practice for all groups, from beginners to fitness professionals.

SPECIAL TRAINING EFFECTS

Training benches represent the connecting link between gymnastic exercises and machine training; strengthening the back is the common denominator. The advantage of gymnastic exercises is that an optimal exercise position can be established and the level of difficulty can thus be adjusted more precisely. If you only perform abdominal crunches on the floor, you will reach a point where an increase in training can only be achieved by increasing the number of times you perform the exercise. With the abdominal bench (page 80), by adjusting the angle of slant of the reclining surface you can substantially change the demand made on the muscles.

Exercises using your own body weight

In addition to the various machines, gymnastic strengthening exercises also have an important place in a training program. Here the body weight itself provides the resistance and thereby determines the right amount of exercise. Many of these exercises were used as the basis for the design of exercise machines.

➤ Tip   Latex band

Before you begin cable training, you should perform gymnastic exercises, ideally using a simple elastic latex band. This teaches you posture amd movement control with gentle resistance from the latex band, which is the best preparation for training with the cable.

Individual body weight provides the precise amoung of training resistance in gymnastic exercises.

Unobtrusive but effective: Among all of the expensive high-tech equipment, benches are a useful training adjunct.

SPECIAL TRAINING EFFECTS

Gymnastic exercises are useful as a preparation and supplement to machine training. As you learn to know your own body, you promote the interaction of the muscles and learn to apply the right level of resistance, all without external weights or additional mechanical resistance. Experienced athletes do not become completely dependent on training machines. If while traveling or on vacation, for example, the accustomed equipment is not available, they can train alternately on the basis of the relevant gymnastic exercises and can keep up their fitness level for many weeks at a time.

Which type of exercise is right for you?

The principle is very simple: the more experienced you are with the machines, the more challenging your training should be. Conversely, for the less experienced, simple, easily controlled machines and exercises are recommended.

➤ **For beginners,** exercise with strength machines is best. Supplementary gymnastic exercises and training benches for exercising the trunk muscles are also recommended. Dumbbell and cable exercises with small weights can be worked in gradually because the paths of motion are well guided or limited and supported at the starting position. Dumbbell and cable exercises with small weights—depending on training progress—can be worked into the program, using smaller weights.

➤ **More advanced** individuals can increasingly use dumbbell and cable exercises to supplement the machine exercises, or replace them with more demanding "free" exercises. Gymnastic exercises and training benches round out the program.

➤ **Experienced athletes** should exploit the entire range of the training possibilities. The combination of exercises is determined most often by which machines provide the greatest training stimulation. If you want to improve your performance in a specific sport, then use those machines that best simulate the special conditions of the sport in question.

Training with resistance tubing, a variant of the latex band, can be performed anywhere and at any time, and exercises all areas of the body.

Nutrition for
Athletes

What the body needs

Well balanced nutrition supports muscle training and helps you on your way to your training goal. While you need carbohydrates and fats as a source of energy for sports, protein provides the conditions for buildup and maintenance of muscle mass. Proteins are a basic building block of life and therefore they have a special purpose in the framework of targeted training.

Positive protein balance

Protein needs can be usually met with normal nutrition. This assumes that adults need from 0.5 through 0.8 gram of protein per pound of body weight for their daily needs. Athletes can increase this level. This is especially true for strength training, when muscle strength is increased and muscle mass is built up. Here the recommendation is for between 0.8 and 1.2 gram—depending on the goal and the training phase. The right amount can be achieved by a targeted selection and combination of commonly available foods. Special protein drinks and protein bars can help, but are not necessary.

THE RIGHT AMINO ACID MIX

Protein provides one of the essential building blocks needed by the body: the amino acids. As proteins are ingested and digested, they are converted into amino acids and then reassembled as the body's own protein. It is especially important to eat the right essential amino acids. A mixed diet of plant and animal protein has proven to be most suitable. These suppliers of protein complement each other optimally in their production of amino acids. Breakfast should consist of a combination of grains and milk products, and at lunch and dinner, menus containing potatoes, legumes (pulses) and lean fish, poultry, or meats are suitable.

LOOK FOR "LEAN PROTEINS"

In addition to the protein and the amino acid mix, the quality of protein-rich foods is particularly important. Figure-conscious individuals should pay special attention to the protein-fat ratio, in order to avoid undesirable side-effects, such as weight gain. For instance, cheese and cold cuts have a very high protein content but at the expense of a correspondingly high amount of fat. Other protein-rich foods, such as low-fat cottage cheese, chicken meat without the skin, fish filets, or lean red meats have a lower fat content.

> ► **Tip**   Losing weight is a question of having a system

The following triple-combination has proven to be an unbeatable recipe for successful weight loss:

1. Individually adjusted endurance training with moderate pulse rate to increase the metabolizing of fats: This teaches the body how to better manage fat metabolism. At rest as well as under strain, the amount of fat burned in comparison to carbohydrate intake is increased; more fat is burned, around the clock. People who successfully perform endurance training can also practice intensive strength training.

2. Targeted muscle build-up training: The more muscles you have at your disposal, the higher the total energy consumption. The basic energy expenditure rate increases with each pound of additional muscle.

3. More carbohydrates, reduced-fat, and high protein nutrition, if possible with lightly reduced total calorie intake: This combination will supply the body with the neccessary nutrients, in order to assist performance and—in combination with movement training— produce the calorie deficit needed for weight loss.

Ideal fitness meal: muesli or granola with milk offers abundant proteins and carbohydrates.

Athletes should be absolutely sure to achieve a positive balance of liquids.

Carbohydrates—optimal fuel for strength training

In order to build up muscles, the body needs sufficient "fuel," which in strength training is mainly provided by carbohydrates. These are found abundantly in whole-wheat bread, whole-wheat pasta, and potatoes. If a serious shortage of carbohydrates is produced, the body's own proteins will be attacked. Instead of building up muscle, muscle will be broken down. It is therefore generally a bad idea to train on an empty stomach.

Protecting the fluid balance

It is very important to have an adequate supply of liquid while training. You must replace the liquids lost through sweat as fast as possible. Furthermore, with an increased protein intake, the kidneys need to be thoroughly rinsed. You should add a good pint or so of liquid relative to the extra protein intake. Apple juice and mineral water or club soda in a proportion of ⅓ apple juice and ⅔ mineral water is an ideal, refreshing drink.

Losing weight with strength training

Muscle training will help you burn fat. The more muscles we have and the more often we use them, the more energy is burned. For this reason as a well-trained individual, you will find it relatively easy to control your body weight. If you train regularly, you will burn calories even while at rest.

GENERATING A CALORIE DEFICIT

Anyone who wants to lose weight must basically generate a calorie deficit, in order to tap into and deplete the fat depots. You can generate this calorie deficit:
➤ by ingesting fewer calories,
➤ by burning more energy through movement,
➤ by a combination of both.
Diets alone won't work because by losing weight the body loses not only fat but also a considerable amount of muscle mass. In addition, the body soon learns how to economize on energy, and immediately stores superfluous calories in its deposit sites. The result is the famous yo-yo effect.

TRAINING ON A DIET

Anyone on a diet should plan meals in such a way as to avoid a growling stomach during training. To protect the body from unnecessary strain, do moderately intensive exercises during training.
The immediate calorie consumption from strength training in comparison to other sports, such as endurance sports, is relatively slight. The obvious benefits will come later, because fat-burning is stimulated over a period of hours, through an increase in the muscle component, which leads to a greater energy throughput over time.

THE GOAL: THE LONG-TERM EFFECT

Losing weight should not be tortuous. It is rather a question of having a system. The importance of strength training was not recognized for a long time, but as an aspect of the long-term benefits it should be included in every weight-loss strategy. Strength training maintains the muscle mass, increases the basic energy throughput, and leads over time to a positive change in the body.

Safety First

The conditions for safe training

Strength training puts demands on the entire body, movement as well as the circulation. The closer you get to your performance limit, the greater the danger of overload. That is why it is important to train safely and to work out the precise amount of training you need.

Exercise patience

Unlike the muscles, the sinews, cartilage, and ligaments have a lower blood supply and therefore need longer to adjust to new phases of training. For this reason, in the early weeks, beginners should ideally train with light to moderate resistance or weights. This recommendation also goes for advanced gym-goers who are trying out new machines or exercises.

The warm-up

Warming up is important, not only for flexibility but also for the circulatory system, as the following example clearly shows: A person goes to the gym immediately after work, feeling stressed out. Since there is not much time, he or she does not perform an adequate warm-up, but instead just swings under the first available dumbbell stand. Even here, there is no time for a slow work-up to the appropriate weight. Without preparation, this individual puts a heavy weight on the bar, and lifts it twelve times with maximum force. This puts a terrible strain on the circulation, since it has to go from practically zero to one hundred percent. In addition, if mistakes are made in respiration (see breathing, page 23), short-term, very high blood pressure sets in, which could be fatal if the heart is not in perfect condition.

For strength training the rule is: every movement must be carefully prepared. The more intensively you train, the more important this basic rule. An adequate warm-up before each training session is a must!

WARMING UP AND STRETCHING

The best way to start the warm-up is to engage the circulation, for instance with five to ten minutes on the ergometer, treadmill, or crosstrainer, with light to medium resistance. This gently stretches the large muscle groups, in order to prepare them in a targeted way for the strain that is to come.

➤ Stabilization test

Before you start training, perform the following quick test, if possible with the help of a partner. The test shows how well you can stabilize your posture by controlling the pelvis. The result is important for the choice of exercises to be used to actively stabilize the body. This is especially true in the case of exercises to be performed in a standing position using free dumbbells or cable pulls.

This is how the test is done:

Get down on all fours (page 90) and balance out your body. Now raise your knees in parallel one to two inches (no more!).

Pay attention to your position, keeping it stable by actively tensing the trunk muscles. Your partner should observe the position of the back and pelvis, which should stay neutral and show no signs of compensation.

➤ **Task 1:** Lift one leg off the floor and stretch it backward in an extension of the spine.

➤ **Task 2:** Stretch out the arm straight ahead on the opposite side to the leg, the right arm and the left leg, then the left arm and the right leg.

A good warm-up on the crosstrainer enhances the peformance of the muscles and reduces the risk of injury.

Safety with a medical check

Another basic rule for safe strength training is that training must be adjusted to the individual capacity for performance and state of health. In order to stay on the safe side, anyone engaged in fitness training over 35 should have a regular sports medicine checkup, which should concentrate on checking the heart. This way, hidden risks will be revealed, most of which can be eliminated before they become serious problems due to overloading. The same applies for people using movement machines, especially if the person suffers from known weaknesses in the back or the large joints. A doctor should be consulted in this case in order to see if there are reasons why strength training is inadvisable or whether special precautions need to be taken.

When to train?

Clearly, training should help the body, not harm it. Since the body in training is always performing beyond its normal level, training should only be attempted under the most favorable circumstances.

➤ If the body is weakened because of a **cold** or flu, for instance, it needs all the energy it can get in order to deal with the infection as quickly as possible. Intensive training would only mean additional stress and could, in the most serious case, become dangerous. Under these conditions, it is best to wait out the illness until the main symptoms, especially the fever, have subsided.

➤ If you have **movement problems**, you should also be careful when experiencing even slight pain and put less strain on the relevant joint or body part. This does not mean that you should abandon strength training entirely, it should be enough to omit the particular exercise or exercises that cause you pain and replace them with others. Good personal trainers can give you valuable tips on how to do this. Generally you should never train into the pain.

➤ Pay attention to how you **feel** on the day you train. If you feel less fit and ready to perform on that day, scale down the amount of training you do. This will pay off in the long run, much more than stubbornly adhering to the demands of a training plan. Training should challenge you but not degenerate into stress. A pleasantly tired feeling after training is completely normal, but you should never feel uncomfortable or ill.

Test evaluation:

➤ **Level A:** The starting position balance can not be easily maintained as soon as one leg is raised.

What to do: You have inadequate body stabilization. Refrain for a while from performing exercises in a standing position, with free dumbbells or on cable machines, or only do them using minimal weights. Your body stabilization can best be improved with exercises using just your own weight.

➤ **Level B:** The starting position balance can easily be maintained when one leg is raised.

What to do: Your body is quite well stabilized. Depending on performance level, you can work exercises into your program without relying too much on machines (free weights and cable exercises).

➤ **Level C:** The starting position can be maintained with one leg and one arm raised.

What to do: you have excellent stability. Use it to your advantage and perform increasingly complex exercises. The entire exercise repertoire is at your disposal.

A Muscle Training
Overview

The ten most important strength training benefits

Individually adapted strength training can be recommended in every phase of life, from youth to old age, because muscle training is one of the most important factors in improving the performance and quality of life, and creating a good figure.

1. Improvement in muscle strength

First of all, training improves the interplay of the muscles (intermuscular coordination). In addition, with more advanced training intensity, the muscles learn to make greater use of the muscle fibers (intramuscular coordination). A firming up of the tissue becomes visible and, above all, the muscle mass increases. The extent of muscle growth depends greatly on the muscle-building hormones, such as testosterone. For this reason, men generally increase their muscle size more than women do.

2. Burning more calories

Calorie consumption increases dramatically with every extra pound of muscle mass—around the clock! People who train regularly find it easier to control their weight. Bear this in mind: Those who have a higher proportion of muscle also weigh more, because muscle is relatively heavy in comparison with body fat. This has nothing to do with being overweight.

3. Muscles improve posture

Slack muscles make the body look slack, while disproportionately developed muscles can skew posture and look uneven. Well developed muscles will enhance your figure.

4. Protection against injury

Well developed muscles surround the body like a shell. They protect it against collisions and falls. The muscles allow for the joints to interact smoothly and counteract the danger of overloading the back; the large joints are increasingly protected.

5. Anti-aging effects

Without concerted strength training, muscle mass begins to decrease at the age of 30. This reduction is not primarily a question of age, but is largely due to an inadequate amount of exercise. Older people who engage in strength training can be fitter and stronger even than untrained younger people. Correctly applied strength training is therefore the real optimal anti-aging formula.

Well trained muscles protect the body when playing sports with a high risk of injury, such as inline-skating.

6. Stable bones

Osteoporosis, or inadequate formation or decrease of bone mass, is becoming increasingly common, not just in women but even in men. The latest research results show that amount of movement is decisive in how well bone matter is built up and maintained. The first three decades of life are the most important: the greater the peak bone mass during this period, the greater will be the protection for the subsequent phases of life. Strength training does not just help preventatively, however, it also has a rehabilitational effect, in that it can slow down and reduce the reduction in bone density. In addition, strong muscles protect the joints from trauma.

7. Positive effects for diabetics

As with endurance training, in strength training improvement in insulin sensitivity can be achieved. This is an important precondition for the regulated use of blood sugar and therefore an important contribution to the prevention of late onset diabetes mellitus, a disease of the metabolism. Diabetics who exercise can also reduce their dependence on medication for the control of the disease.

8. Greater body awareness

Intense focus on the body also teaches body awareness. Strength training gives you the chance to recognize your own body signals and to act upon them. This is especially true for sensitivity to strain and control of movement.

9. Plus points for heart patients

Through an increase in maximum strength, the general stress caused by everyday living as well as from sports becomes more bearable. For heart patients, this means that if they are well trained they will reach their maximum training levels at a later stage. This buffer can function as an important protective factor against circulatory system overload.

10. General performance

Anyone who has had a thorough strength-training session knows the feeling they have after a workout. You are relaxed yet fully alert at the same time. The figure is more attractive and your gait is more erect. The more regularly you train, the more such short-term effects will become lasting. You will never want to do without these positive effects ever again.

The pulse watch (near right)—a valuable device, and not just for athletic heart patients.

A good figure is always related to good physical posture (far right).

Ten typical mistakes and how you can avoid them

If you look around a gym or health club, you will inevitably recognize a series of typical mistakes. The following checklist will help you to perform your exercises in as error-free a way as possible. Quality before quantity!

1. Cold start

Just like any motor, the body needs to warm-up. The more intensive the training, the more rigorously you should perform the warm-up (page 30).

2. Too high training weight

The cardinal mistake in fitness training is putting too much weight on the barbell or machine block due to overambition. The "training effect" will be registered, but there will be no measurable increase in strength. On the contrary, as a rule, heavy training weights come at the expense of ligaments, tendons, and joints. It is better to use lighter weights and to train more precisely.

3. Unharmonious movements

Nothing has a more negative effect from a bio-mechanical point of view than strain caused by excess speed. If you accelerate suddenly or curb the movement with a swing, greater forces come into play, and the joints will not be able to tolerate them over time. This means that you may be able to handle heavier weights, but you will not achieve a better training effect. The countermeasure is to use a smooth, even range of movement as standard, whenever you exercise.

4. False axis adjustment

If, for instance, on the seated press or leg extension machine (pages 42 and 44) the roll over or under the lower legs moves out of position, the axis between the joint and machine will be incorrect. The countermeasure is to find the point of rotation of the machine and to align it with the joint. Let the trainer help you.

5. Lack of posture control

When the movement itself—considered in isolation—is performed correctly, but the posture is incorrect, actively stabilize your body. Keep your head straight as an extension of the spine, and remember the direction of your gaze will guide your posture and movement.

Conscious posture and movement control in front of a mirror will help you avoid typical errors.

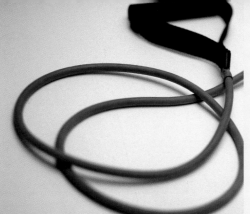

In selecting the right weight, less can often be more.

Small devices, such as this resistance tubing, can be used to complement the training at home.

6. False movement ranges

The fullest range of range of movement should be used in most exercises. However as a variation, it can sometimes make sense to emphasize certain parts of the exercise. For instance, end contractions or multiple repetitions in the last third of the movement cycle, in order to additionally stimulate the muscle in the phase of greatest foreshortening. Be careful not to neglect the rest of the movement, however. On the other hand, it also makes sense with some exercises to hold the end-point of the movement, in order to avoid strain on the ligaments, tendons, and joints.

7. Irregular training

People who train intensively for one week and take a break the next, and then the next, will not have much success, even if they use the fourth week to try and make up for the training they have missed. The key to success lies in continuity, not in sporadic fits of strenuous exercise.

8. Monotonous training

The muscles need so-called supra-threshold stimulation in order to continually adapt themselves. This means that if the training is not systematically increased or varied, one day the muscle will no longer be stimulated and will fail to react with an increase in strength. This does not mean, however, that weights should be constantly increased. It is much more important to vary and change the exercises and the exercise routine.

9. Incorrect timing

The great majority of people actively engaged in training place emphasis on the lifting phase and neglect the release phase, bringing down the weight too fast and in an uncontrolled manner. The eccentric function of the muscles is inadequately addressed. The countermeasure is a deliberate extension of three to four seconds in the return phase.

10. Abrupt finish

It is important to give the body a chance to "coast" or to cool off. This improves the conditions for regeneration, which is crucial for training to be a success, because the body does not adapt during the loading phase, but only during recovery.

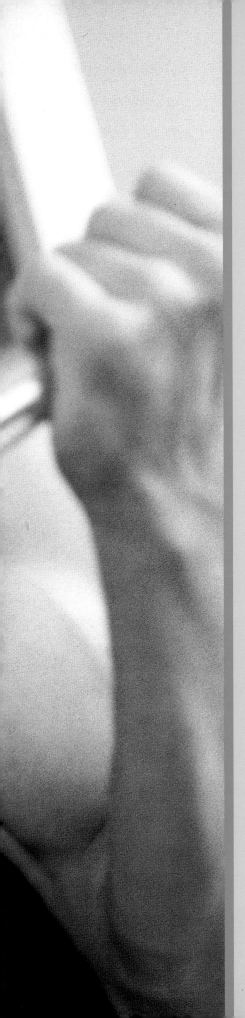

The
Exercises

This section gives you the most effective exercises for all the important muscle groups, divided into seven major body areas. Detailed photographs, combined with anatomical illustrations, show exactly which exercise activates which muscle, whether you are using a machine, dumbbells and barbells, cable machines, training benches, or performing gymnastic exercises. The exact description of the starting position and the movement, exercise variations, and common errors section will help you perform each exercise correctly.

Setting up the
Exercise Pool

An overview of the description categories

Main and supporting muscles

In naming the muscles in most of the exercises, you will find that the main muscles are differentiated from the supporting muscles. This will show you which muscles lead the movement, and which perform synergetic and supporting functions. The dividing line is not entirely rigid, however. There are also exercises (such as the leg extension machine, page 42), for which no supporting muscles are indicated, because the movement is concentrated on the main muscle group.

Certain muscle groups are best grouped together to give you a complete picture. For instance, the catchall term "shoulder blade muscles" includes five different muscles (page 119). In addition, with most of the upper body dumbbell and cable machine exercises, the detailed listing of the individual forearm muscles has been omitted.

Important: We have taken care to show the main and supporting muscles for every exercise. However, sometimes this can not be illustrated, because thee are underlying muscles that are obscured by those on the surface, or the muscles called into play are on the other side of the body. There are therefore muscles listed in the overview that are not shown in the illustrations. This applies to the pages dealing with the body area (page 39), hips and buttocks (page 55), stomach (page 73), back (page 91), chest (page 107) shoulders (page 119), and arms (page 139).

Evaluation

All exercises are evaluated using a five-stage system, in order to make it easier for you to select them. One point represents the lowest and five the highest value.

➤ **Demands:** This characterizes the degree of technical difficulty of the relevant exercise. The more complex the movement, the less it is guided and secured by the machine, the higher the value in this category. Those with less experience in training should begin with exercises that are less demanding.

➤ **Training effectiveness:** This measures how strongly the muscles are activated by an exercise.

➤ **Stress potential:** The stress potential evaluation is designed to draw attention to the specific dangers that may be inherent in the exercise.

Starting position and movement

The starting positions and the execution of the movements of all the exercises are described in detail. The "neutral-zero-method" is used for the body angle values. The basic reference point is the normal, erect posture, from which all angles are defined as the zero degrees position. If from this position the arm is raised to a horizontal position, for example, there will be a 90-degree angle at the shoulder joint. A knee angle of 80 degrees (the recommended sitting position) means that the knee joints are bent at slightly less than a right angle.

Variations, important tips

Under the heading "Exercise variations" you will find tips for how you can easily modify and vary the exercise and what consequences this will have for the muscle stimulation. Finally, in the category "Important tips" special information and typical errors are indicated.

Legs

The following exercises train the muscles of the thigh and lower leg in a targeted fashion. They are especially responsible for the movement and stabilization of the knee and ankle joints.

THE THIGH

The largest muscle on the front of the thigh is the quadriceps *(Quadriceps femoris)*. Its four separate muscles enable the knee joint to be stretched. The inner component of the muscle is especially important, because it contributes substantially to joint stabilization.

The muscle at the back of the thigh is the *ischiocrurale musculature*, which is formed from the thigh biceps muscle *(biceps femoris)*, and the semitendinosus and semimembranosus muscles. All three muscles work as hip extensors as well as knee flexors.

THE LOWER LEG

Most lower leg exercises are for the calf muscles. The calf muscles include the triceps surae, which is subdivided in the gastrocnemius muscle and the soleus muscle. The gastrocnemius muscle extends from the upper ankle joint to the knee joint. It functions as a powerful bending mechanism in the ankle joint and has a stabilizing effect on the knee joint.

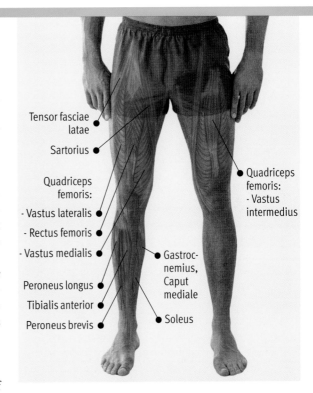

Tensor fasciae latae
Sartorius
Quadriceps femoris:
- Vastus lateralis
- Rectus femoris
- Vastus medialis
Peroneus longus
Tibialis anterior
Peroneus brevis
Quadriceps femoris:
- Vastus intermedius
Gastrocnemius, Caput mediale
Soleus

The muscles of the thigh and lower leg as seen from front and rear.

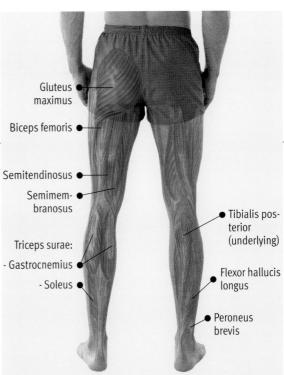

Gluteus maximus
Biceps femoris
Semitendinosus
Semimembranosus
Triceps surae:
- Gastrocnemius
- Soleus
Tibialis posterior (underlying)
Flexor hallucis longus
Peroneus brevis

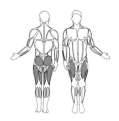

MAIN MUSCLES:
thigh quadriceps/biceps muscles
(Quadriceps/Biceps femoris), large buttock
muscle *(Gluteus maximus)*, semi-
membranous/tendinosus muscle

SUPPORTING MUSCLES:
adductor group, *(Tensor fasciae latae)*,
gastrocnemius muscle, soleus muscle

Seated leg press

1. Starting position

Place the feet at about the width of
the hips, with the feet on the tread
parallel or slightly turned outward.
Stabilize the body by tensing the
trunk muscles and holding onto
the handles. The entire back
should be in contact with the back
support.

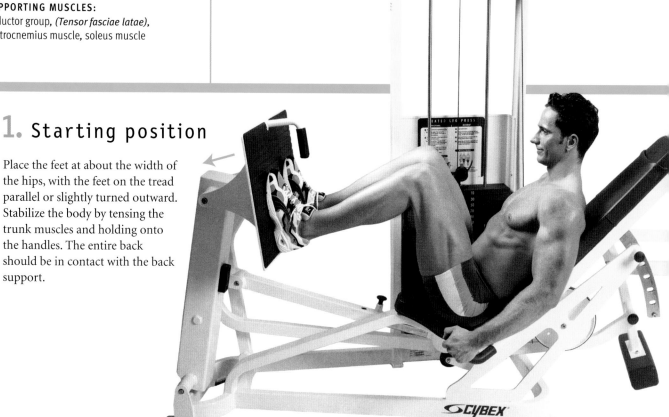

Exercise variations:

➤ The steeper the angle of the back support, the greater the strain on the trunk musculature and the lower
the demand on the *Quadriceps*. You achieve the greatest training effect for the *Quadriceps* by using the
leg press in a recumbent position.

➤ You can get comparable effects by adjusting the feet on the tread: the higher you place the feet, the
wider the hip angle and the more the you will engage the trunk muscles. The lower you place your feet,
the narrower the hip angle and the more you will engage the *Quadriceps*.

Evaluation:

The exercise activates a range of muscles, especially the *Quadriceps* and the buttock muscles. Since the muscles are strengthened by the interaction, training with the seated leg press is very effective. At the same time, it requires good movement coordination, especially if training is performed with heavy weights.

Suitability:

Using the right technique and appropriate weight this is an appropriate exercise for all target groups.

COORDINATION DEMANDS:
● ● ● ◐ ○

TRAINING EFFECTIVENESS:
● ● ● ● ●

STRESS POTENTIAL:
● ● ● ◐ ○

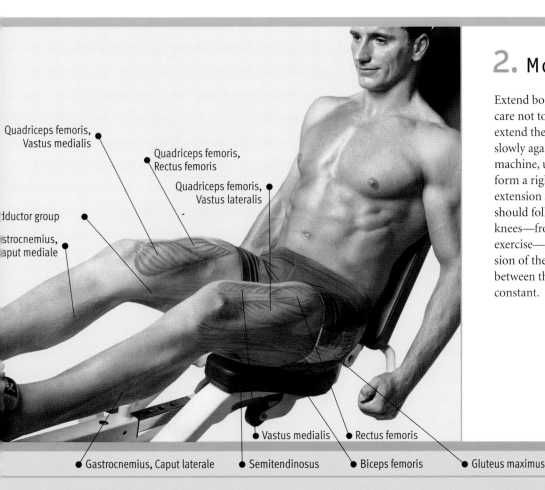

Quadriceps femoris, Vastus medialis

Quadriceps femoris, Rectus femoris

Quadriceps femoris, Vastus lateralis

Adductor group

Gastrocnemius, Caput mediale

Vastus medialis • Rectus femoris

Gastrocnemius, Caput laterale • Semitendinosus • Biceps femoris • Gluteus maximus

2. Movement

Extend both legs evenly (but take care not to overextend or even fully extend them). Then bend the legs slowly against the resistance of the machine, until the knee joints to form a right angle. The entire extension and bending movement should follow a straight line. The knees—from the standpoint of this exercise—are guided as an extension of the feet. The distance between the knees should be kept constant.

Important tips:

➤ Keep the upper body straight during the entire movement.
➤ Don't pull the shoulders forward or round the back.

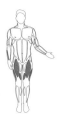

Seated leg extension

MAIN MUSCLES:
thigh quadriceps muscle *(Quadriceps femoris)*: straight, inner, outer, and middle thigh muscles *(Rectus femoris, Vastus medialis, lateralis,* and *intermedius)*

SUPPORTING MUSCLES:
none

1. Starting position

Choose a sitting position in which the axis of the knee is an extension of the machine axis. Adjust the back support so that the entire back is supported evenly. Stabilize your starting position by pulling lightly on the handles. Then straighten the upper body.

Exercise variations:

➤ You can also do this exercise one-legged. The advantage is that possible performance differences between the right and left leg will be obvious and can be evened out in a targeted fashion.

➤ Increasing the angle of tilt of the back support means the straight thigh muscles *(Rectus femoris)* are increasingly activated. However the danger of slipping into a hollow back position is also increased.

Evaluation:

This flexible machine is designed especially to address the *Quadriceps* —next to the knee extension, this muscle group also supports the flexing of the hips.

Suitability:

Thanks to the guided movement, the exercise is relatively simple. However, it does not reflect typical daily movements and is therefore in the long run only recommended as a supplement to other more complex exercises.

COORDINATION DEMANDS:
● ○ ○ ○ ○

TRAINING EFFECTIVENESS:
● ● ● ◐ ○

STRESS POTENTIAL:
● ● ● ● ○

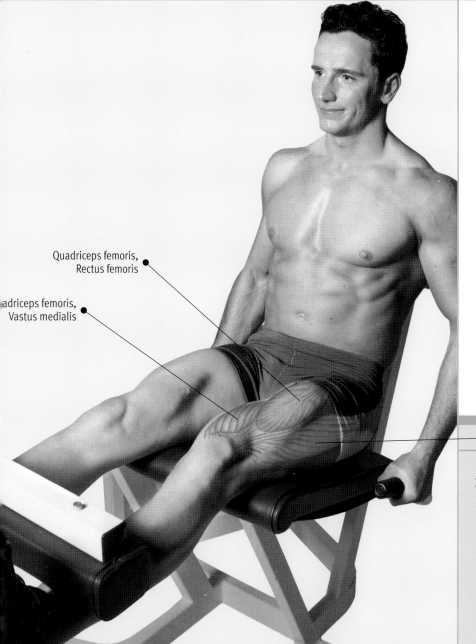

Quadriceps femoris,
Rectus femoris

adriceps femoris,
Vastus medialis

Quadriceps femoris, Vastus lateralis

2. Movement

Lift both legs in an even movement until the knee joints are fully extended (take care not to overextend them). Then guide the legs back until the knees form a right angle, but no further.

Important tips:

➤ Inconvenient loading of the knee joint can occur, causing increased slipping of the joint surfaces.

➤ Avoid compensatory movements in the back and in the shoulder area.

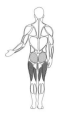

Seated leg curl

MAIN MUSCLES:
thigh biceps muscle *(Biceps femoris)*, semitendinosus muscle, semimembranosus muscle

SUPPORTING MUSCLES:
tailor muscle *(sartorius)*, slender thigh adductor *(Gracilis)*, large buttocks muscle *(Gluteus maximus)*

1. Starting position

Adjust the seat surface and the back support so that the knee axis is in an extension of the machine axis. The entire back should be in contact with the back support. The thighs are held in position from above by the padding. Tense the buttock muscles to stabilize the upper body. Then sit up straight by pulling on the handles.

Exercise variations:

➤ Depending on the foot position, it is possible to produce different accentuations of the muscles being exercised: Turning slightly inward (inward rotation) emphasizes the activity of the semimembranous muscle and the semitendinosus muscle, while turning the feet out engages the thigh biceps muscles.

➤ This exercise can also be performed one-legged.

Evaluation:

A simple, machine-guided exercise for targeted strengthening of the leg-flexing muscles. The disadvantage of this seated exercise is that you will be sitting on the very muscles that are being trained. They have to be stretched out, however, when they are contracted and should therefore not be cramped.

Suitability:

The seated leg curl is good for all target groups, but over time only as a supplement for exercises performed standing or lying down, where the muscles can move freely.

COORDINATION DEMANDS:
● ○ ○ ○ ○

TRAINING EFFECTIVENESS:
● ● ● ◐ ○

STRESS POTENTIAL:
● ◐ ○ ○ ○

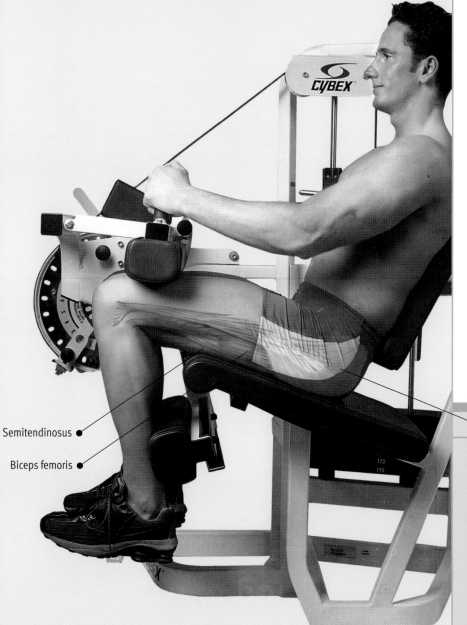

Semitendinosus

Biceps femoris

Gluteus maximus

2. Movement

Pull back both lower limbs in an even movement, without swinging. The heel should lead back toward the buttocks. Hold briefly at the reversal point and then slowly release—against the machine pressure—to return to the starting position. The movement should stop just before the extension of the knee joints.

Important tips:

➤ Always keep the buttocks stable and upright, i.e., do not round the back or make it hollow.

➤ To avoid leg cramps, you can pull back lightly on the toes.

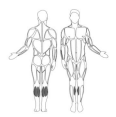

MAIN MUSCLES:
calf biceps muscle *(Gastrocnemius)*, soleus muscle *(Soleus)*

SUPPORTING MUSCLES:
posterior tibialis *(Tibialis posterior)*, long and short calf muscles *(Peroneus longus* and *brevis)*, flexor hallucis longus, flexor digitorum longus

Seated calf press

1. Starting position

Place the balls of the feet parallel at the same width as the hips on the tread. Adjust the seat distance so that the legs are slightly bent, but the knees are fully extended! Grip the handles at the sides and sit up straight by tensing the buttock muscles.

Exercise variations:

➤ In order to intensify the exercise you can also pre-stretch the calf muscles. You can do this by starting the movement from a position with your feet pulled back.

➤ The one-legged alternative is recommended.

Evaluation:

This special exercise for the isolated training of the calf muscles is very simple, but because of the short range of movement, it requires concentration.

Suitability:

For all target groups.

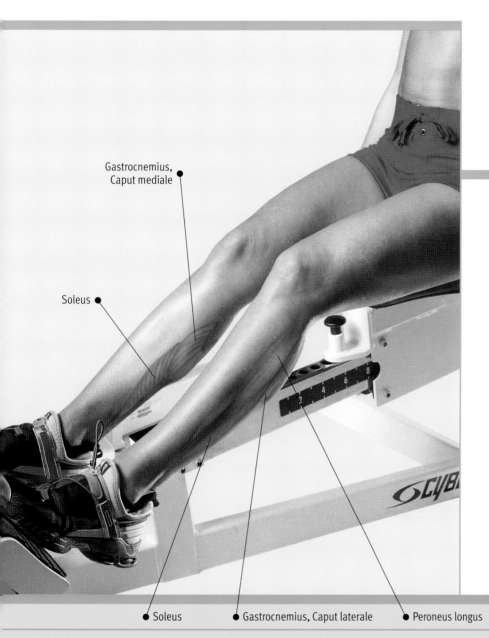

Gastrocnemius, Caput mediale

Soleus

Soleus   Gastrocnemius, Caput laterale   Peroneus longus

COORDINATION DEMANDS:
● ○ ○ ○ ○

TRAINING EFFECTIVENESS:
● ● ● ● ○

STRESS POTENTIAL:
● ● ○ ○ ○

2. Movement

Press the tread slowly forward using the calf muscles to do so. Ensure that the pressure is the same from both feet. Hold the exercise briefly at the reversal point and then return slowly and deliberately, without letting the weight jerk. The legs should remain in a neutral position during the entire movement, with slightly bent knee joints.

Important tips:

➤ Pay special attention to the symmetrical positioning of the feet. The feet should be parallel to each other or turned slightly outward.

➤ Combine the training on this machine with stretch exercises for the calf muscles.

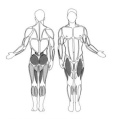

MAIN MUSCLES:
thigh quadriceps muscle *(Quadriceps femoris)*, large buttocks muscle *(Gluteus maximus)*, lower back muscles *(Erector spinae)*, semimambranous and semitendinosus muscles

SUPPORTING MUSCLES:
thigh biceps muscle *(Biceps femoris)*, thigh adductor *(adductor group)*, calf biceps muscle *(Gastrocnemius)*, soleus muscle

Barbell squat

1. Starting position

Assume a stable position, the legs somewhat wider than the hips, and turn your feet outward (with an outward rotation of the hip joints). The upper body should be bent slightly forward and the back straight, showing the slight natural inward curve at the lumbar region. Hold your head in line with the back, while thrusting the breast-bone *(sternum)* out slightly. Stabilize the barbell symmetrically on the shoulders.

Exercise variation:
➤ Experienced athletes can perform deeper knee-bends. The knees should be bent so deeply that the thighs are approximately perpendicular. This leads to increased activity of the *Quadriceps*, but also to increased strain on the knee joints.

Evaluation:

The squat is certainly the most effective compound exercise (one in which demands are placed on many muscle groups at the same time) for the calves, thighs, buttocks, and back muscles (sling stretch). Effective, safe training requires a clean movement technique which should first be learned without weights.

Suitability:

For beginners under professional supervision.

COORDINATION DEMANDS:
● ● ● ● ○

TRAINING EFFECTIVENESS:
● ● ● ● ●

STRESS POTENTIAL:
● ● ● ● ○

Gluteus maximus

Quadriceps femoris, Vastus medialis

Adductor group

Quadriceps femoris, Vastus lateralis

Quadriceps femoris, Rectus femoris

Biceps femoris

Semitendinosus

Gastrocnemius

Soleus

Semimembranosus

2. Movement

Begin the movement with your legs bent, as if you were sitting on a high stool. Let your buttocks sink back slowly but in a controlled movement, until the knees are bent at roughly a right angle. The entire movement then proceeds in a line, in which the knee—from the standpoint of the person doing training—continually moves in an extension of the feet (knee-foot alignment).

Important tips:

➤ The back must be kept straight and stable for the entire movement.

➤ Do not pull the shoulders forward or round the back under any circumstances. If you perform the exercise correctly, the squat will also serve as a strengthening exercise for the back.

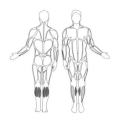

MAIN MUSCLES:
calf biceps muscle *(Gastrocnemius)*, soleus muscle

SUPPORTING MUSCLES:
posterior tibialis *(Tibialis posterior)*, peroneus longus and brevis langer, flexor hallucis longus, flexor digitorum longus

Calf lift with dumbbells

1. Starting position

Stand on a step or comparable raised surface. Position the balls of the feet at the width of the hips in their neutral position on the tread or step. The feet should point forward or be turned out slightly. Stabilize the upright body posture by actively tensing the buttock muscles. Select the dumbbells that are right for your level of performance and hold them firmly at shoulder height next to the body. Deliberately tense the muscles in the shoulder region.

Exercise variations:

➤ The exercise can also be performed one-legged, reducing the weight of the dumbbells accordingly. You can also do it without dumbbells and just lift your own body weight.

➤ In order to increase the movement radius and for targeted training from a pre-stretched position (this is relevant for many kinds of sports that require jerky movements), you can start carefully with your heels lowered to below the edge of the step.

Evaluation:

The exercise is performed on a step, using very small radius of movement (lifting and lowering the heels). It has to be performed slowly and using concentration.

Suitability:

With the weight appropriate for the person training, the exercise is good for all levels of performance.

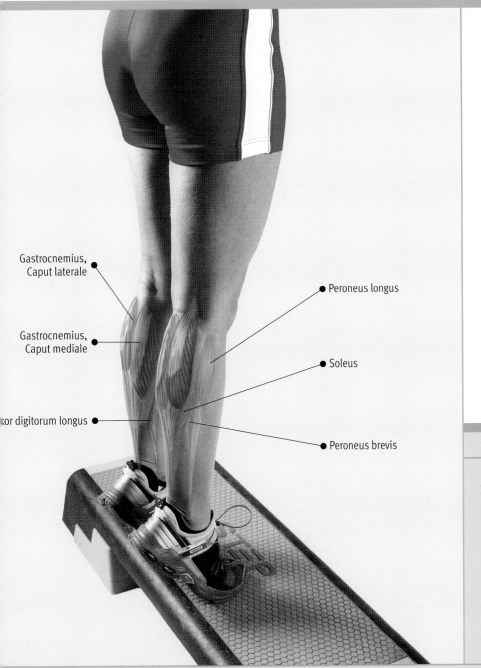

Gastrocnemius, Caput laterale

Gastrocnemius, Caput mediale

...or digitorum longus

Peroneus longus

Soleus

Peroneus brevis

2. Movement

Stand on tiptoe as far as possible without swinging upward. Hold the position briefly at the highest point and bring the heels down slowly and deliberately back to the starting position.

Important tips:

➤ With this exercise it is especially important to warm up well beforehand.

➤ Begin with a low weight and increase it slowly.

MAIN MUSCLES:
thigh biceps muscle *(Biceps femoris)*, semimam-branous, and semitendinosus muscles

SUPPORTING MUSCLES:
lower back muscle *(Erector spinae)* in the lumbar vertebrae region, tailor muscle *(Sartorius)*, slender thigh adductor *(Gracilis)*, large buttock muscle *(Gluteus maximus)*

Leg curl lying on the stomach

1. Starting position

Fasten the collar just above the ankle bone and then lie on your stomach lengthwise in front of the lower pulley of the cable machine. The head should be resting on the crossed arms in an extension of the back. Support the pelvis with a rolled-up hand towel in order to avoid a hollow back. The toes should point toward the pulley, with the heels toward the buttocks. In order to stabilize the pelvis, actively tense the buttock muscles.

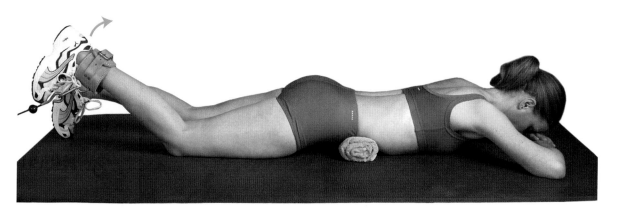

Exercise variation:

➤ A slight inward rotation of the lower leg emphasizes the activity of the *Semimembranosus* and the *Semitendinosus*, while a slight outward rotation increasingly activates the *Biceps femoris*. Use the variations only for a short time or sporadically because they can induce asymmetrical strain on the joints.

Evaluation:

An intensive, technically demanding exercise for training the back leg muscles (knee flexing function). It should be performed under professional supervision and checked in the mirror.

Suitability:

For experienced athletes.

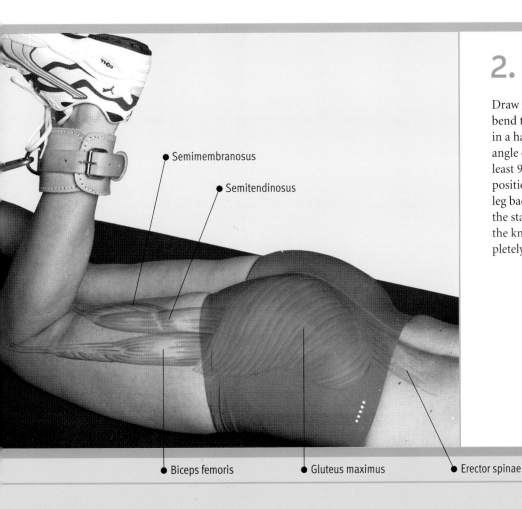

● Semimembranosus

● Semitendinosus

● Biceps femoris   ● Gluteus maximus   ● Erector spinae

2. Movement

Draw in the the toes somewhat and bend the leg with the heel forward in a harmonic movement. The angle of the knee joint should be at least 90 degrees. Maintain the final position briefly and then guide the leg back against the cable pull to the starting position. This prevents the knee joint from being completely extended. Change sides.

Important tips:

➤ Pay special attention to straight-line motion. It always runs parallel to the leg lying on the ground. The heel moves as an extension to the back of the leg.

➤ When the knee joint is stretched, avoid pulling, because the angle of traction used here is not good for the muscle tendons which could become sore.

COORDINATION DEMANDS:
● ● ● ● ○

TRAINING EFFECTIVENESS:
● ● ● ◐ ○

STRESS POTENTIAL:
● ● ◐ ○ ○

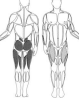

MAIN MUSCLES:
thigh biceps muscle *(Biceps femoris)*, large buttocks muscle *(Gluteus maximus)*, lower back muscle *(Erector spinae)* in the lumbar vertebrae area, semimambranous and semitendinosus muscles

SUPPORTING MUSCLES:
thigh biceps muscle *(Quadriceps femoris)*, hip abductor *(Tensor fasciae latae)*

Pelvic lift in the back position

Evaluation:

A technically demanding and intensive strength exercise, which uses your own body weight. It requires good stabilization of the buttocks and pelvis.

Suitability:

For advanced gymnasts.

Tensor fasciae latae • — Biceps femoris

Gluteus maximus •

• Erector spinae — • Semitendinosus — • Semimembranosus

Starting position and Movement

Lie on your back on a mat. Bend one leg at about a right angle and shift your weight to the sole of your foot. Lift and extend the other leg with the foot pulled slightly back. Stabilize the body with the arms and hands at the sides of the body.

Raise and lower the pelvis with the strength of the bent leg. The pelvis is thereby lifted so that the leg, hips, and upper body are in line with one another. Now, lower the pelvis again until the extended leg is just above the floor. The muscle tension must be maintained the entire time. Change sides.

Exercise variation:

➤ This exercise can also can be performed completely statically without vertical movement pelvic movement. The end position with raised pelvis is held for several seconds.

Important tips:

➤ Actively tense the abdominal muscles to support the pelvis (avoid a hollow back!).

➤ Since the movement can only be performed in a small radius, the exercise requires concentration.

Hips and Buttocks

The hip joint makes it possible for the leg to move in all directions and planes. Hip bending *(flexion)*, is distinguished from hip extension *(extension)*, spreading *(abduction)*, and pulling *(adduction)*, as well as inward and outward rotational movements.

While the hip flexor *(Iliopsoas)* can be trained according to need, the train the hip extensors should rather be trained in a targeted way. This is especially true for the large buttock muscle *(Gluteus maximus)*, because as the most important support for the pelvis, it has a major effect on the curvature of the spine.

ABDUCTORS AND ADDUCTORS

The abductors are located on the outside of the thighs. They are the counterpart of the adductors and direct the spreading movement of the leg. The adductor group located on the inner thigh makes it possible to pull the thigh toward the body. The adductors, next to the *Gluteus maximus,* are among the strongest muscles of the body, because in addition to the pelvis they also stabilize the posture and allow for an upright gait.

In order to train all functions of the abductors and the adductors, the movements should be combined with inward and outward rotations of the leg. This is especially beneficial when performing exercises on machines that require a pulling motion.

Hip and buttock muscles: The right training supports the natural curve of the spine.

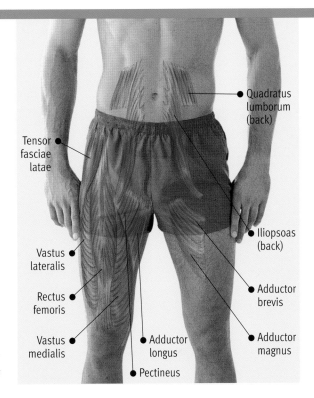

- Quadratus lumborum (back)
- Tensor fasciae latae
- Iliopsoas (back)
- Vastus lateralis
- Rectus femoris
- Adductor brevis
- Vastus medialis
- Adductor longus
- Adductor magnus
- Pectineus

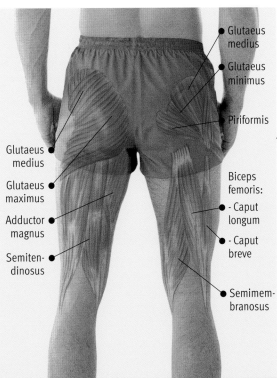

- Glutaeus medius
- Glutaeus minimus
- Piriformis
- Glutaeus medius
- Glutaeus maximus
- Biceps femoris:
  - Caput longum
  - Caput breve
- Adductor magnus
- Semitendinosus
- Semimembranosus

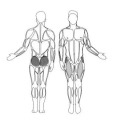

MAIN MUSCLES:
gluteus medius and gluteus minimus,
adductor group *(Tensor fasciae latae)*,
piriformis muscle

SUPPORTING MUSCLES:
rectus femoris, large buttocks muscle

Lever seated
hip abductor

1. Starting position

Position yourself on the machine
so that the hip joint axis is in line
with the machine axis. Adjust the
padding above the knee joint as far
as possible. The entire length of the
back should be in contact with the
back support. Tense the trunk
muscles (to provide stability) and
adjust the upper body by pulling
on the handles.

Exercise variation:

➤ Some machines are fitted with additional padding under the knee. If pressure is evenly applied by the
lower legs against the padding, the activity of the *Tensor fasciae latae* is strengthened. At the same time,
this could also lead to shearing load in the knee joint (uneven loading between the thigh and lower leg),
which is bad for the cartilage. Therefore this variation should be closely controlled with reduced weight
if need be.

Evaluation:

A simple yet effective exercise for the spreading muscles (abductors). The construction of the machine should allow for a carefully guided range of movement. Avoid compensatory movements in the area of the lumbar region.

Suitability:

For all target groups, regardless of ability.

COORDINATION DEMANDS:
● ◐ ○ ○ ○

TRAINING EFFECTIVENESS:
● ● ● ● ◐

STRESS POTENTIAL:
● ◐ ○ ○ ○

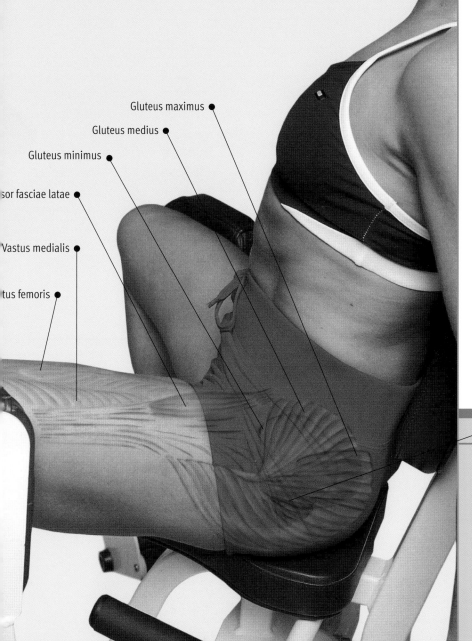

Gluteus maximus ●

Gluteus medius ●

Gluteus minimus ●

sor fasciae latae ●

Vastus medialis ●

tus femoris ●

● Piriformis

2. Movement

Spread the legs as far apart as possible with uniform pressure of the thighs. Hold the position briefly at the reversal point and then guide the legs slowly back to the starting position against the pressure of the lever arms. The return movement should not go so far that the weights disengage and the legs touch each other. Maintain the muscle tense the whole time.

Important tips:

➤ Never swing the body during the exercise.

➤ Ensure that during the spreading movement the lumbar vertebrae are always in contact with the back support.

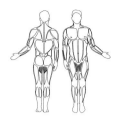

MAIN MUSCLES:
inner thigh adductors *(Adductor brevis, longus* and *magnus)*, slender thigh adductor *(Gracilis)*, pectineus muscle

SUPPORTING MUSCLES:
none

Lever seated hip adductor

1. Starting position

If the machine has one, use the entry support. Position yourself on the machine so that the axis of rotation of the hip joint rotation is in line with the axis of the machine. Ensure that the padding is as high as possible above the knee joint; the entire back should be in contact with the back support. Tense the trunk muscles (for stability) and adjust the upper body by pulling on the handles.

Exercise variation:

➤ Some machines are equipped with additional padding under the knee. With discrete pressure of the lower legs against the padding the activity of the *Gracilis* (slender thigh muscle) is improved. This could lead, however, to shearing load in the knee joint (uneven loading between the thigh and lower leg), which is bad for the cartilage. This variation should therefore be closely checked and if necessary, performed with reduced weight.

Evaluation:

A simple but effective exercise for the adductors. The machine construction should allow for a carefully guided range of movement and targeted training.

Suitability:

For all target groups.

COORDINATION DEMANDS:
● ○ ○ ○ ○

TRAINING EFFECTIVENESS:
● ● ● ● ◐

STRESS POTENTIAL:
● ● ◐ ○ ○

- Gracilis
- Adductor longus
- Pectineus

2. Movement

Bring both legs to about the width of the hips, applying equal pressure to the thighs. The lever arms should not touch each other. Then move both legs outward against the braking action of the lever arms, ensuring that there is no compensatory movement in the area of the pelvis and back. Hold the position briefly at the reversal point and then press the legs back to the middle position. Keep the muscles tense the entire time.

Important tips:

➤ Never swing the body during the exercise, movement must always be controlled.

➤ Ensure that during the spreading movement the lumbar vertebrae are always in contact with the back support.

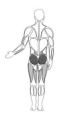

MAIN MUSCLES:
large buttock muscle *(Gluteus maximus)*

SUPPORTING MUSCLES:
gluteus medius and gluteus minimus, thigh
biceps *(Biceps femoris)*, semimembranous
and semitendinosus muscles, lower back
muscles *(Erector spinae)* in the area of the
lumbar vertebrae

Lever kneeling
hip extension

1. Starting position

Adjust the support padding so that
the pelvis is supported by it in a
stable position. Then support the
upper body on the forearm
padding and grab the hand grips.
The back should be in line with the
head in an extension of the back
and the gaze directed downward.
The stabilizing leg should rest on
the padding provided for it. Place
the other leg with the entire sole of
the foot on the tread. Before you
begin the movement actively tense
the buttock muscles.

Exercise variation:

➤ Repeat the exercise in smaller ranges of movement near the end position (end contractions).

Evaluation:

A very effective and well guided exercise, especially good for the buttock muscles. The body position is held stable and counteracts an overextension of the back (hollow back).

Suitability:

Suitable for all levels, especially in the context of a back-strengthening program.

COORDINATION DEMANDS:
● ● ◑ ○ ○

TRAINING EFFECTIVENESS:
● ● ● ● ◑

STRESS POTENTIAL:
● ● ◑ ○ ○

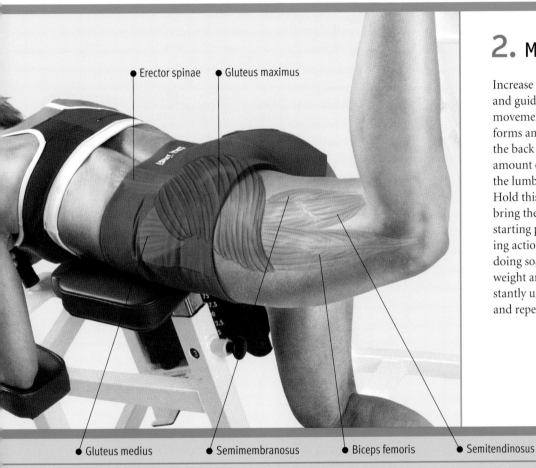

● Erector spinae   ● Gluteus maximus

● Gluteus medius   ● Semimembranosus   ● Biceps femoris   ● Semitendinosus

2. Movement

Increase the pressure on the tread and guide the leg in a controlled movement upward until the thigh forms an extension of the back and the back has reached the normal amount of curve in the region of the lumbar vertebrae (lordosis). Hold this position briefly and then bring the leg back down to the starting position against the braking action of the machine. When doing so, do not let go of the weight and keep the muscles constantly under tension. Change legs and repeat the exercise.

Important tips:

➤ Always keep the back straight. The movement should not be carried out too high because otherwise the pelvis can shift, causing the back to become hollow.

➤ Always keep the pelvis symmetrical (do not tip to one side or turn it outward).

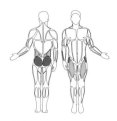

MAIN MUSCLES:
gluteus medius and gluteus minimus,
adductor group *(Tensor fasciae latae)*,
piriformis muscle

SUPPORTING MUSCLES:
rectus femoris, great buttocks muscle, leg
muscles of the supporting leg (statically
loaded)

Cable hip abductor

1. Starting position

Position the collar directly above
the ankle or—if the pulley height
can be adjusted—just above the
knee joint (see the exercise variations). Stand sideways with the
knee slightly bent next to the lower
pulley of the cable machine. Slip a
flat board under the supporting
leg, so the training leg can freely
be pulled forward (from the floor).
Stabilize the body by supporting
yourself sideways and tensing the
buttock muscles.

Exercise variations:

➤ If you turn the point of the foot inward (inner rotation of the hip joint), the gluteus medius and minimus
are emphasized.

➤ By turning the foot a little outward the gluteus maximus is accentuated. However as a rule you should
train in the neutral position.

➤ If a height adjustable pulley system is available, it is recommended to fasten the collar directly above the
knee. This minimizes the strain on the knee and you can train with larger weights.

Evaluation:

In comparison with the abductor machine (page 56) a very demanding exercise for training the spreading muscles. The body must be well stabilized in order to carry it out. Do not overlook the relatively high level of strain on the standing leg, which must balance out the entire movement.

Suitability:

Not for beginners.

COORDINATION DEMANDS:
● ● ● ● ○

TRAINING EFFECTIVENESS:
● ● ● ● ○

STRESS POTENTIAL:
● ● ● ◐ ○

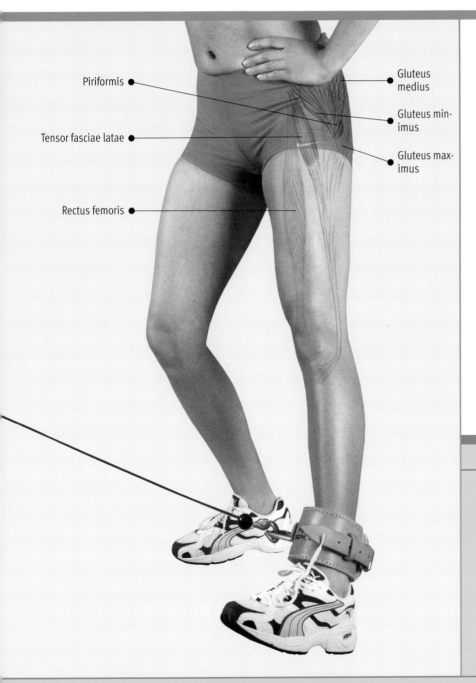

Piriformis ●

Tensor fasciae latae ●

Rectus femoris ●

Gluteus medius ●

Gluteus min-imus ●

Gluteus max-imus ●

2. Movement

Guide the leg that is being trained outward in an even, straight line as far as possible. In the basic exercise the point of the foot always points forward. The spreading movement should be stopped as soon as the compensatory movement in the hips begins. Then slowly guide the leg against the pull of the cable back to the starting position next to the standing leg (or for pre-stretching, crossed at about 10°). Change sides and repeat the exercise.

Important tips:

➤ The strain on the standing leg with this exercise is often under-estimated. Therefore it is advisable to do it with fewer repetitions.

➤ Pick a weight that is not so great that it provokes compensatory movements in the hips and back region.

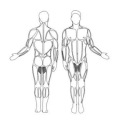

MAIN MUSCLES:
inner thigh muscles *(Adductor brevis, longus* and *magnus)*,
slender thigh adductor *(Gracilis)*,
pectineus muscle

SUPPORTING MUSCLES:
leg muscles of the supporting leg (statically loaded)

Cable hip adductor

1. Starting position

Position the collar directly above the ankle or to the extent the height of the pulley can be adjusted, just above the knee joint (see the exercise variations). Stand sideways with the knee slightly bent next to the lower pulley of the cable machine. Slip a flat board under the supporting leg, so that the training leg can be freely (from the floor) be pulled forward. Stabilize the body by supporting yourself sideways and tensing the buttock muscles.

Exercise variations:

➤ The exercise can also be performed with the foot turned slightly outward (outer rotation in the hip joint). As a rule, however, you should train in a neutral foot position, with the tips of the toes pointing forward.

➤ If a height-adjustable pulley system is available, fasten the collar directly above the knee. This position minimizes the strain on the knee and enables you to train with larger weights.

Evaluation:

In comparison with the abductor machine (page 58), this is a very demanding exercise for training the spreading muscles. The body must be very well stabilized in order to perform it. Do not overlook the relatively high level of strain on the standing leg, which must balance out the entire movement.

Suitability:

Because of the heavy demands made by this exercise, it is not well suited for beginners.

COORDINATION DEMANDS:
● ● ● ● ○

TRAINING EFFECTIVENESS:
● ● ● ● ○

STRESS POTENTIAL:
● ● ● ● ○

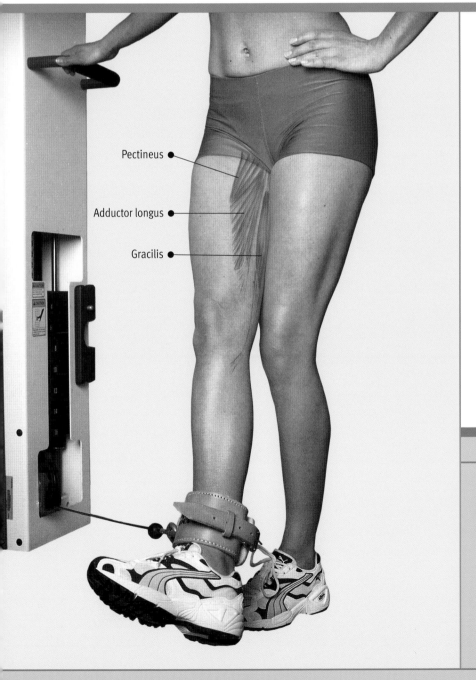

Pectineus

Adductor longus

Gracilis

2. Movement

Guide the leg that is being trained in an even, straight line toward the supporting leg, without touching it. To increase the range of movement, the moving leg can cross the supporting leg by up to 10 degrees (see photo). The leg should then be slowly guided against the pull of the cable. The spreading movement should be stopped as soon as compensatory movement in the hips begins. The tips of the toes should always point forward in the basic exercise. Change legs and repeat the exercise.

Important tips:

➤ In this exercise, the strain on the standing leg is often underestimated. It is therefore advisable to perform it with fewer repetitions.

➤ Select a weight that is not so heavy that it causes compensatory movements in the hips and back region.

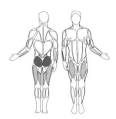

MAIN MUSCLES:
gluteus maximus, gluteus medius, gluteus minimus

SUPPORTING MUSCLES:
thigh biceps *(Biceps femoris)*, semitendinosus, semimembranosus, lower back muscles *(Erector spinae)* in the area of the lumbar vertebrae, thigh quadriceps muscle *(Quadriceps femoris)*

Hip extender with cable

1. Starting position

Fasten the leg collar attached to the cable of the lower roll. Kneel in front of the cable pull and support yourself on your forearms. Your back should be straight and stabilized and you should be on all fours. Tense the trunk muscles and lift the knee of the training leg slightly.

Exercise variation:

➤ The entire movement proceeds with the hip and knee joints bent under the body and continues until the leg is extended. As a variation, the range can be shortened by reducing the bending motion. The knee could be allowed to point down at a right angle instead of diagonally forward.

Evaluation:

A complex exercise for the targeted training of the hip extensor muscles, especially the buttock muscles.

Suitability:

For advanced training because individuals should have a good range of movement.

COORDINATION DEMANDS:
● ● ● ◐ ○

TRAINING EFFECTIVENESS:
● ● ● ◐ ○

STRESS POTENTIAL:
● ● ◐ ○ ○

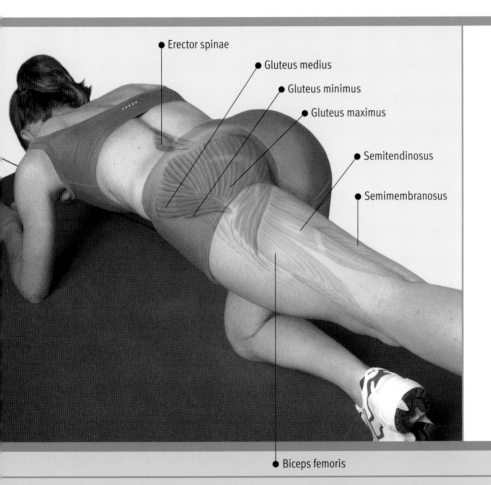

- Erector spinae
- Gluteus medius
- Gluteus minimus
- Gluteus maximus
- Semitendinosus
- Semimembranosus
- Biceps femoris

2. Movement

Start the exercise by pulling back the training leg and guiding it under the upper body. From this position, straighten the leg with the sole of the foot forward, until it is lifted in a line with the back and the back is allowed to curve normally in the area of the lumbar vertebrae (lordosis). The cable will run back in a line between the arms and legs. Now guide the leg back to the starting position against the pull of the cable. Change legs and repeat.

Important tips:

➤ Pay special attention to ensuring there is a straight-line extension of the leg.

➤ Emphasize the full extension phase and hold the movement briefly at the reversal point.

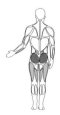

MAIN MUSCLES:
large buttocks muscle *(Gluteus maximus)*

SUPPORTING MUSCLES:
thigh biceps *(Biceps femoris)*,
semitendinosus and semimembranous
muscles, lower back muscles *(Erector spinae)*
in the area of the lumbar vertebrae

Reverse leg lift with cable

1. Starting position

Fasten the foot collar just above
the ankle and position yourself
with a straight, slightly forward
with bent upper body in front of
the machine. Tense the trunk muscles and hold the upper body
firmly using the handlebar. Bend
the knee of the supporting leg
slightly (do not overextend it).

Exercise variation:

➤ The collar can also be attached above the knee joint by positioning the pulley correspondingly higher.
  This single joint variation prevents the knee joint from being overloaded.

Evaluation:

An effective exercise for the trunk muscles. It requires a stability throughout the entire body.

Suitability:

With the appropriate control, and using a mirror, recommended for all target groups.

COORDINATION DEMANDS:
● ● ● ○ ○

TRAINING EFFECTIVENESS:
● ● ● ◐ ○

STRESS POTENTIAL:
● ● ● ○ ○

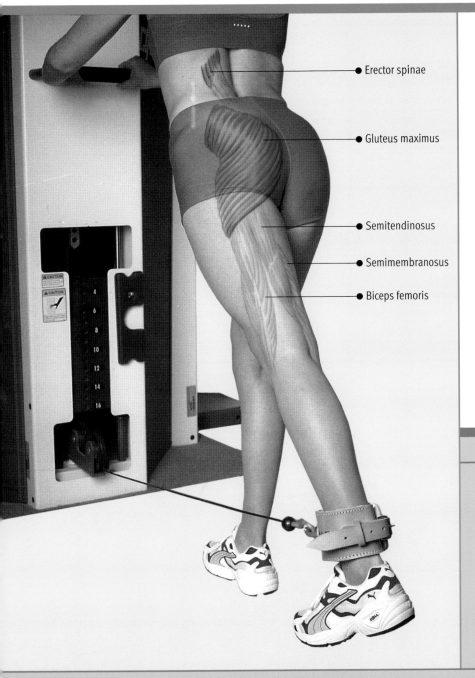

- Erector spinae
- Gluteus maximus
- Semitendinosus
- Semimembranosus
- Biceps femoris

2. Movement

Guide the training leg with the heel leading in a straight line past and behind the supporting leg. The movement can be extended as long as there is a normal swing in the back in the area of the lumbar vertebrae (lordosis). Then bring back the leg against the pull of the cable until it is just in front of the supporting leg. Change sides and repeat the exercise.

Important tips:

➤ If possible, slip a flat board under the supporting leg, so that the training leg is free to move backward, i.e., free from contact with the floor.

➤ Avoid swinging and compensatory movements.

COORDINATION DEMANDS:

TRAINING EFFECTIVENESS:

STRESS POTENTIAL:

MAIN MUSCLES:
gluteus medius and gluteus minimus, tensor fasciae femoris *(Tensor fasciae latae)*, piriformis muscle

SUPPORTING MUSCLES:
rectus femoris, large buttocks muscle *(Gluteus maximus)*, quadratus lumborum muscle, lower back muscle *(Erector spinae)*

Side-lying abductor lift

Evaluation:

The spreading muscles (abductors) in both legs are simultaneously strengthened. While the upper leg is being lifted, the leg on the floor must statically balance out the movement.

Suitability:

The exercise is recommended for more advanced exercisers.

- Gluteus medius   - Tensor fasciae latae

- Rectus femoris

Starting position and movement

Lie on your side on a mat. Bend the lower leg in an approximate right angle to the back and support your upper body with your forearm. The elbow should be extended directly underneath the shoulder. Head, trunk, and legs should all be in line. In order to support the position, the upper arm can be extended past the head.

Now spread the upper leg as far as possible upward, but not so far that compensation in the area of the pelvis or back sets in. Guide the leg back to the starting position, just above the supporting leg, but without touching it. Muscle tension must be maintained the entire time. Change legs and repeat the exercise.

Exercise variation:

➤ Well trained individuals can extend the lower leg and support themselves with the edge of the foot (long lever), instead—as shown—of bending the leg (short lever). In this variation, the spreading muscles of the supporting leg are under heavy strain. This also involves a greater strain on the knee joint, so caution is advised.

Important tips:

➤ This exercise is only effective if a rock-hard starting position is held, so that the pelvis does not drop or rotate.

Side supported abductor lift

COORDINATION DEMANDS:
● ● ● ○ ○

TRAINING EFFECTIVENESS:
● ● ● ○ ○

STRESS POTENTIAL:
● ○ ○ ○ ○

MAIN MUSCLES:
short, long, and large inner thigh adductors
(*Adductor brevis, longus* and *magnus*),
slender thigh adductor (*Gracilis*), pectineus
muscle

SUPPORTING MUSCLES:
none

Evaluation:

In this exercise, the ends of the inner thigh adductors are flexed and bent. Since the path of movement is very short, the exercise must be performed slowly and with concentration.

Suitability:

For all levels.

Starting position and movement

Lie on your side on a mat and bend the arm you are lying on. The head lies on the bent arm and is thereby an extension of the back. Bend the upper leg at a right angle support the knee with a rolled up towel so that the pelvis does not twist. The lower leg lies outstretched in extension of the back with the foot pulled.

Raise and lower the lower leg over a short range of movement. The foot should always be flexed as shown. Hold the position briefly at the highest point. The leg should only drop so far that it is not touching the mat, ensuring muscle tension is maintained. Change sides and repeat the exercise.

Adductor longus

Gracilis

Exercise variation:

➤ For a change, the exercise can also be performed with the toes turned slightly outward and/or inward.

Important tips:

➤ Stabilize the pelvis and the trunk by additionally tensing the abdominals.

➤ Avoid jerky movements.

COORDINATION DEMANDS:

● ● ● ◑ ○

TRAINING EFFECTIVENESS:

● ● ● ○ ○

STRESS POTENTIAL:

● ● ◑ ○ ○

MAIN MUSCLES:
large buttock muscle *(Gluteus maximus)*

SUPPORTING MUSCLES:
thigh biceps muscle *(Biceps femoris)*, semi-tendinosus muscle, semimembranous muscle lower back muscles *(Erector spinae)* in the area of the lumbar vertebrae

Hip extension on all fours

Evaluation:

This exercise works well if the range of movement is small. It must be performed slowly and with concentration to be effective.

Suitability:

Primarily for intermediate and advanced exercisers.

Gluteus maximus ●

Erector spinae ●

● Semitendinosus

● Semimembranosus

● Biceps femoris

Starting position and movement

Stabilize the body on all fours on the fore-arms. The hands should point forward and the tips of the toes to the rear. The elbows should be at right angles to the shoulders. Keep the upper body straight and the head in an extension of the back. Look down-ward. The pelvis and shoulder girdle must be parallel to the floor.

Bend the leg at a right angle and pull on the foot slightly. Lift the leg toward the ceiling without changing the angle of the knee. The upward movement (hip extension) contin-ues until the natural curve in the area of the lumbar vertebrae has been reached (lordo-sis). Hold this position briefly and then low-er the leg by about 45 degrees. Change legs and repeat the exercise.

Exercise variation:

➤ The upper leg with the knee bent is brought toward the chest and then, led by the heel, is extended back. It is then an exact extension of the back.

Important tips:

➤ Stabilize the back by tensing the abdominal muscles.

➤ Avoid swinging movements.

Abdomen

Trained abdominals—consisting of vertical, horizontal and diagonally running muscles—straighten up the pelvis and ensure a good posture. Together with the back muscles they form a kind of trunk muscle sheath that lends stability to the back and protects it from overloading. The separate sections of the straight abdominals together go to produce the famous washboard or six-pack belly, an important aesthetic goal for many athletes. Conversely, physical inactivity, especially for the abdominals, has a clearly debilitating effect, which takes its toll on posture, performance ability, and the figure. Targeted abdominal muscle training is therefore especially recommended for health, athletic, and aesthetic reasons.

COMBINATION EXERCISES

In the following pages you will find the best exercises for addressing the varied areas and functions of the abdominals. This chapter, in particular, contains a large number of exercises that can be performed at home, using just your own body weight because especially in the case of abdominals, gymnastic exercises are as valuable as machine exercises and some are even superior. Practice has shown that a mixture of different exercise types is the most effective strategy.

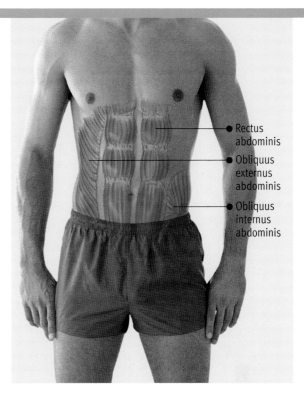

- Rectus abdominis
- Obliquus externus abdominis
- Obliquus internus abdominis

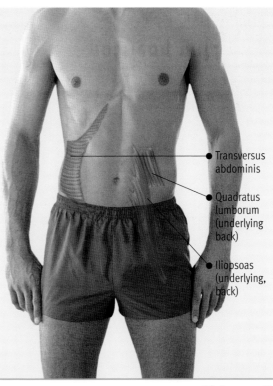

- Transversus abdominis
- Quadratus lumborum (underlying back)
- Iliopsoas (underlying, back)

The abdominal muscles—the illustration above shows the surface muscles while the one below shows the underlying muscles.

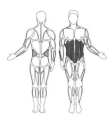

MAIN MUSCLES:
rectus abdominis muscle *(Rectus abdominis)*, external and internal oblique abdominis *(Obliquus externus* and *internus abdominis)*

SUPPORTING MUSCLES:
transverse abdominis *(Transversus abdominis)*

Seated abdominal trainer

1. Starting position

Adjust the seat so that the axis of rotation of the machine is at about navel height and runs coaxially through the lumbar region. Hips and knee joints should be bent, and the back straight. Position the lever arm of the machine at breast-bone height. Actively tense the abdominals and pull the chin slightly toward the chest. The body should follow the movement of the head and not the other way around.

Exercise variation:

➤ As a variation, you can perform short repetitions in the end position (end contractions) and then move the upper body in a slow, controlled manner back to the starting position.

Obliquus extern abdominis

Obliquus internu abdominis

Rectus abdominis

Evaluation:

A classic machine exercise for training the abdominals, especially the rectus abdominis. In contrast to gymnastic abdominal muscle exercises without machines, the advantage is that resistance can be adjusted to individual performance. Both types of exercise are equally effective.

Suitability:

As an abdominal muscle exercise that can be performed without a machine, the exercise requires little coordination ability and is therefore well suited to people with relatively little experience.

COORDINATION DEMANDS:
● ● ◐ ○ ○

TRAINING EFFECTIVENESS:
● ● ● ◐ ○

STRESS POTENTIAL:
● ● ◐ ○ ○

2. Movement

Roll the upper body vertebra forward. Only roll so far forward that no or very little bending in the hips occurs. Guide back the trunk against the pressure of the lever arm in the reverse order: the back should be straightened vertebra by vertebra.

Important tips:

➤ Common mistake: If the movement is primarily initiated by bending the hip joint, instead of rolling with the trunk, the exercise will lose most of its effectiveness.

➤ Bring the breastbone and pelvis toward each other.

➤ Support the movement as little as possible with shoulders or arms. The only movement should derive from the activity of the abdominal muscles.

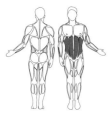

rectus abdominis muscle (*Rectus abdominis*), external and internal oblique abdominis (*Obliquus externus* and *internus abdominis*)

SUPPORTING MUSCLES:
transverse abdominis (*Transversus abdominis*)

Cable crunch

1. Starting position

Take two handles (or a rope) from the high pulley of a cable machine and pull them close to the upper body. Crouch down with the upper body straining against the pull of the cable. The direction of the pull of the cable should run upward at a steep angle. Actively tense the trunk muscles and pull in the chin slightly toward the chest. Look diagonally toward the floor. In the starting position, you will not be fully upright, but rather in a half-crunch position and the trunk will be somewhat rolled in, so that abdominal muscle tension can be maintained.

Obliquus externus abdominis

Rectus abdominis

Obliquus int[…] abdominis

Exercise variations:

➤ You can also choose an upright kneeling position. The pelvis will then be very slightly bent.

➤ In order to train the oblique abdominals in a targeted way, combine the movement with a slight rotation in the shoulder axis.

Evaluation:

In contrast to the crunch without cable pull, the degree of difficulty can be individually adjusted by altering the weight on the machine. Since the trunk is not held in place by any device, the body must be actively stabilized, requiring a certain amount of movement experience.

Suitability:

Primarily for more advanced muscle-trainers.

COORDINATION DEMANDS:
● ● ● ● ○

TRAINING EFFECTIVENESS:
● ● ● ◐ ○

STRESS POTENTIAL:
● ● ◐ ○ ○

2. Movement

Roll the upper body so that it goes into a crunch movement forward and downward. This directs the entire pull over the abdominals. The pelvis remains stable and does not bend forward with the movement. The movement stops as soon as the pelvis itself starts to move. Hold the position briefly at the point of reversal and then return slowly to the starting position against the pull of the cable (half-crunch position).

Important tips:

➤ Ensure that the movement is guided exclusively by the abdominals and that no other muscles are involved.

➤ The hands should only hold the handles to the body but should not be involved in the pulling motion.

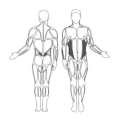

MAIN MUSCLES:
quadratus lumaorum muscle, external and internal oblique abdominis *(Obliquus externus* and *internus abdominis)*

SUPPORTING MUSCLES:
rectus abdominis, lower back muscles *(Erector spinae,* especially *Longissimus* and *Ilio-costalis)*—all muscles that are located opposite the pulling side

Cable side-bend

1. Starting position

Position yourself sideways to the lower pulley of the cable machine. Stabilize the feet a little further apart than the hips, with the knees slightly bent. Lean the upper body in a smooth curve to the side. It is important not to bend the hips. Hold the handle of the cable pull with your arm outstretched and the palm facing the body. Hold the back of your head loosely with your free hand, with the elbow pointing outward in an extension of the shoulder. Now tense the trunk muscles in order to actively stabilize the body position.

Rectus abdominis ●

Obliquus externus abdominis ●   Obliquus internus abdominis ●

Exercise variation:

➤ You can intensify the exercise by performing some short radius repetitions in the end position (end contractions).

Evaluation:
An easily adjustable exercise for training the side of the body and shaping the waist. If possible perform in front of a mirror.

Suitability:
With controlled movement, suitable for all levels of training.

COORDINATION DEMANDS:
● ● ● ○ ○

TRAINING EFFECTIVENESS:
● ● ● ○ ○

STRESS POTENTIAL:
● ● ● ○ ○

2. Movement

Move the trunk sideways in a uniform movement and bend it with deliberate involvement of the lateral trunk muscles on the opposite side of the cable. At all times, the head is held as an extension of the trunk. Your bent arm stays relaxed. At the point of reversal, hold the position briefly and then move back against the pull of the cable to the starting position. Change sides.

Important tips:

➤ The entire movement takes place in one plane. It is very important to avoid compensating the shoulder and/or the pelvis with other parts of the body.

➤ Always look toward the front.

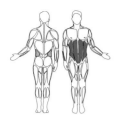

MAIN MUSCLES:
rectus abdominis muscle *(Rectus abdominis)*, external and internal oblique abdominis *(Obliquus externus* and *internus abdominis)*

SUPPORTING MUSCLES:
transverse abdominis *(Transversus abdominis)*

Abdominal bench

1. Starting position

Choose the angle of the bench surface that allows you to perform the number of technically clean repetitions that you want. The same goes for the positioning of the arms and hands (see the exercise variations). If the machine has a lordosis pad, adjust the back so that the lumbar vertebrae are lying exactly over the padding and are correspondingly supported. From a prone position, bend the legs at a right angle.

Exercise variations:

➤ You can change the degree of difficulty of the exercise by changing the angle of the bench or the position of the arms and hands. In ascending order, from easy to difficult:
  - Hands next to the body, pointing forward
  - Hands folded over the stomach
  - Hands placed on the side of the head or neck (never use them to pull the head!)
  - Arms outstretched behind the head.

➤ If you want to emphasize the oblique abdominals, combine the movements by slightly turning the shoulder axis.

Evaluation:

Next to the high-tech machines, the simple bench has long since proven itself as an effective training aid. The advantage of the bench as opposed to the twisted crunch performed on the floor (page 88/89) is that with the angle of the bench you can successively adjust the training intensity.

Suitability:

For all levels of performance.

COORDINATION DEMANDS:

TRAINING EFFECTIVENESS:
● ● ● ● ○

STRESS POTENTIAL:
● ● ○ ○ ○

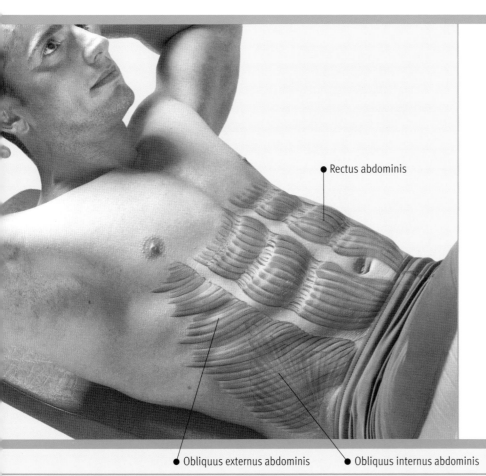

Rectus abdominis

Obliquus externus abdominis   Obliquus internus abdominis

2. Movement

Lift slightly the head and shoulders. Now roll up the upper body in a concentrated manner and without swinging sideways, until the shoulder blades lose contact with the padding. The head should form a line with the trunk. Hold the final position for a moment and then return slowly to just before the starting position. Do not rest your head. The tension in the abdominal muscle area must be maintained constantly.

Important tips:

➤ Sitting up so that the upper body is straight does not create any significant additional effects in training of the abdominal muscles but it increases the load on the disks in the area of the lumbar vertebrae.

➤ Ensure that you do not pull your head forward too much by looking upward.

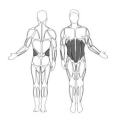

MAIN MUSCLES:
rectus abdominis muscle *(Rectus abdominis)*, external and internal oblique abdominis *(Obliquus externus* and *internus abdominis)*, transverse abdominis *(Transversus abdominis)*

SUPPORTING MUSCLES:
hip flexors *(iliopsoas)*

Reverse abdominal trainer

1. Starting position

Lie on your back on the bench so that the lumbar vertebrae are supported by the convex padding (lordosis pad). A rolled up towel under the neck will prevent overstretching the neck vertebrae. The legs should be bent at a right angle at the knee joints, while the lower legs are held horizontally in the air. Arrange your arms as shown on the side supports. The arms must be in contact with the padding for the entire time. Before starting the movement, actively tense your abdominals.

Exercise variations:

➤ In order to make the training easier, pull back the knees in the direction of the upper body. Lift the pelvis vertically from this starting position with the lower legs held horizontally.

➤ The exercise can also be performed with outstretched legs. In this variation, the legs led by the sole of the foot are "pushed" up at a right angle.

COORDINATION DEMANDS:
● ● ● ● ○

TRAINING EFFECTIVENESS:
● ● ● ● ○

STRESS POTENTIAL:
● ● ○ ○ ○

Evaluation:

The exercise is designed to work on the lower region of the abdominals. The movement should be performed with minimal deflection. It is demanding from the standpoint of coordination and is very effective.

Suitability:

Primarily recommended for advanced muscle-trainers.

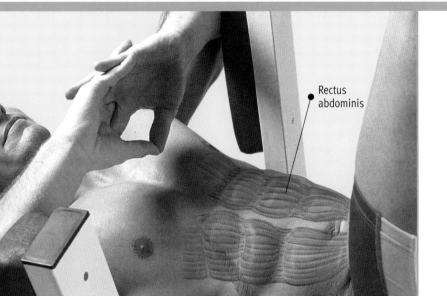

Rectus abdominis

Transversus abdominis

Obliquus internus abdominis

2. Movement

Push the knees straight upward without any swing. The coccyx should lift completely off the bench. The lower legs should stay in a horizontal position. Hold the position at the reversal point for at least a second. Then lower the pelvis again very slowly and deliberately, without letting the coccyx completely touch the bench. The tension in the abdominals must be maintained the entire time.

Important tips:

➤ The arms are not actively involved but should be used for support in the sitting up movement.

➤ Make sure to lower the legs slowly and avoid all swinging movements.

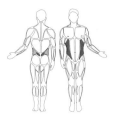

MAIN MUSCLES:
quadratus lumaorum muscle
external and internal oblique abdominis
(*Obliquus externus* and *internus abdominis*)

SUPPORTING MUSCLES:
rectus abdominis, lower back muscles (*Erector spinae*, especially *Longissimus* and *Iliocostalis*)—all muscles that are located opposite the pulling side

Lever side-bend

1. Starting position

Adjust the distance from the tread to the padding so that the pelvic ridge is flush with the edge of the padding. The legs stabilize the position of the whole body. Place the hands loosely on the neck, with the elbows pointing outward in an extension of the shoulder axis. Let the trunk lean over in an even, arc-shaped movement.

Exercise variations:

➤ The flatter the surface on which you lie, the higher the training intensity.

➤ Effectiveness increases if you perform a few repetitions in the lowest position of the body (end contractions).

➤ In order to emphasize the oblique abdominal muscles, the trunk at the shoulder axis can be turned slightly inward while straightening up.

Evaluation:

An important exercise for lateral stability of the trunk. It is only effective, however, if the body is moved sideways and not tilted back and forth.

Suitability:

With professional guidance at the start and performed in front of a mirror, suitable for all levels of training and is highly recommended as part of a back-strengthening program.

COORDINATION DEMANDS:
● ● ● ○ ○

TRAINING EFFECTIVENESS:
● ● ● ● ◑

STRESS POTENTIAL:
● ● ● ◑ ○

Rectus abdominis

Quadratus lumborum (underlying, back)

2. Movement

Draw up the trunk from this position slowly and evenly to the side and tilt it further toward the opposite side. The movement should be directed by the muscle tension in the outer body flank. Hold the head at all times in an extension of the trunk. Always look forward. Change sides.

Important tips:

➤ Ensure that the tilt to both sides occurs evenly, and that there is no buckling in the trunk.

➤ The entire movement should be performed in one plane (sideways tilt). Avoid any swinging movements and any compensation in the hips.

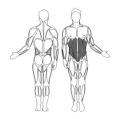

MAIN MUSCLES:
rectus abdominis muscle *(Rectus abdominis)*,
external and internal oblique abdominis
(Obliquus externus and *internus abdominis)*

SUPPORTING MUSCLES:
transverse abdominis *(Transversus abdominis)*

Ab-roller

1. Starting position

Lie on your back on a mat and
position the back of your head on
the neck padding of the ab-roller.
Bend the legs at right angles and
press the heels against the floor.
Hold onto the upper part of the
frame loosely and lean your
upper arms on the arm padding.
Tense your abdominals.

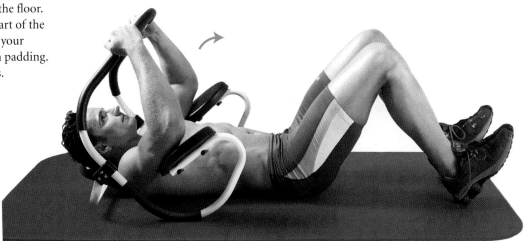

Exercise variations:

➤ If you want to intensify the crunch movement, hold your legs at right angles in the air.

➤ For training the oblique abdominals lean the legs in parallel—knee to knee—
sideways toward the floor. The rolling up movement is performed as in the basic exercise.

Evaluation:

The ab-roller—derived from "abdominals"—is a good machine to use for abdominal training. In comparison with the normal crunch, compensatory movements are practically ruled out.

Suitability:

The machine is especially well suited for beginners and for people with problems in the neck area.

COORDINATION DEMANDS:
◉ ◐ ○ ○ ○

TRAINING EFFECTIVENESS:
◉ ◉ ◉ ○ ○

STRESS POTENTIAL:
◉ ◐ ○ ○ ○

● Obliquus externus abdominis   ● Obliquus internus abdominis   ● Rectus abdominis

2. Movement

Roll the upper body forward with the ab-roller, until the shoulder blades no longer touch the floor. The hands should support the straightening movement as much as is necessary, and no more. The head should rest comfortably relaxed on the neck padding. Hold the position briefly at the reversal point and let the upper body sink back with even abdominal pressure into the starting position.
Roll back only so far, so that the abdominals remain tensed the entire time.

Important tips:

➤ Do not pull the head to the chest, but hold it supported by the neck padding in an extension of the back.

➤ Always guide the movement without swinging and slow down the roll-back on the way down.

➤ The arms are not actively involved in the movement; do not pull the frame forward.

COORDINATION DEMANDS:
● ● ● ◐ ○

TRAINING EFFECTIVENESS:
● ● ● ● ○

STRESS POTENTIAL:
● ● ● ○ ○

MAIN MUSCLES:
external and internal oblique abdominis
(*Obliquus externus* and *internus abdominis*)

SUPPORTING MUSCLES:
rectus abdominis, transverse abdominis
(*Transversus abdominis*)

Twisted crunch

Evaluation:

A standard exercise for training the oblique abdominals that requires a certain measure of basic abdominal strength.

Suitability:

For the above reason, beginners should only perform the exercise with folded arms (see variations).

Obliquus externus abdominis • Obliquus internus abdominis • Rectus abdominis

Starting position and movement

Lie on your back and lift your legs to create a right angle in the hips as well as the knee joint (as if sitting on a stool). Place your hands behind your head, with the elbows pointing outward in parallel. Do not pull on your head.

Now actively tense the abdominals and lift the head, elbows, and shoulders—in that order. As the upper body rolls up, turn the shoulder axis to the side. Hold the end position briefly (the shoulder blades should have no contact with the floor) and then, while maintaining the abdominal tension, let the upper body roll back down slowly. Keep the head and elbows just off the floor. Do not forget to change sides.

Exercise variations:

➤ The easier way
  – guide the arms forward over the floor or fold them over the abdomen
  – bend the legs at a right angle.

➤ To increase the level of difficulty
  – stretch back the outside arm in the end position in an extension of the shoulder
  – lift the pelvis until the coccyx loses contact with the floor.

Important tips:

➤ The elbows should always remain parallel to the shoulder axis in the basic exercise. Do not pull the elbows and shoulders forward when rolling up.

➤ Avoid all swinging movements and make sure to breathe evenly.

➤ Train both sides equally.

Diagonal crunch

MAIN MUSCLES:
Rectus abdominis muscle (*Rectus abdominis*),
external and internal oblique abdominis (*Obliquus externus* and *internus abdominis*)
transverse abdominis (*Transversus abdominis*)

SUPPORTING MUSCLES:
hip flexors (*iliopsoas*)

Evaluation:
A challenging exercise for the complex training of the entire abdominals, with which all main functions of the abdominals are activated.

Suitability:
The exercise requires a good feeling for movement and already well trained abdominals. It is therefore only for very advanced individuals.

Starting position and movement

Lie on your back and lift the legs so as to create a right angle in the hips as well as in the knee joint (as if sitting on a stool). Actively tense the abdominal muscles. Now lift the head slightly and begin to roll up the upper body. Pull one knee in the direction of the upper body and stretch the hand on the opposite side in the direction of the ankle. The other arm should be stretched back and the other leg extended forward diagonally. The upper body slightly turns with the rolling up movement. Perform this movement alternating continuously on both sides, without resting the head on the floor. The abdominals should remain completely tensed at all times.

● Rectus abdominis   ● Obliquus externus abdominis

Exercise variation:
➤ The further the arm is stretched back, flat over the floor, the greater the leverage effect will be and the more intense the exercise.

Important tips:
➤ Perform the exercise in a controlled way without any swinging movement.
➤ During the rolling up phase the head stays in an extension of the upper body and the chin is not pulled to the chest.

COORDINATION DEMANDS:
● ● ● ○ ○

TRAINING EFFECTIVENESS:
● ● ● ◐ ○

STRESS POTENTIAL:
● ● ○ ○ ○

MAIN MUSCLES:
rectus abdominis muscle *(Rectus abdominis)*, external and internal oblique abdominis *(Obliquus externus* and *internus abdominis)*, transverse abdominis *(Transversus abdominis)*

SUPPORTING MUSCLES:
hip flexors *(Iliopsoas)*

Isometric floor press

Evaluation:

In this exercise the abdominals are tensed and strengthened statically, that is without moving them. It is useful as a supplement or an alternative to the crunch exercises.

Suitability:

Good for beginners.

● Rectus abdominis

● Transversus abdominis

Starting position and movement

Go down on all fours: The back should be straight and the head in line with the back. Look downward. Place the hands at shoulder width with slightly bent elbows beneath the body. Tense the trunk muscles in order to stabilize the starting position. Lift both knees very slightly (1–1½ inches from the floor) while the trunk is balanced out, supported by the hands and feet. You can intensify the abdominal tension by trying to pull the hands toward the knees, as if dragging them along the floor. The position of the back should not change. Hold the tension for a few seconds and then let down the knees briefly. Repeat the sequence as appropriate to your level.

Exercise variations:

➤ While the hands "pull" forward, the knees can be "pushed" slightly forward to create a crunch position between shoulders and pelvis.

➤ By increasing the hip angle, you can intensify the exercise. The knees should slip further back. However this greatly increases the danger of a hollow back position.

Important tips:

➤ The knees should only be very slightly raised, so that abdominal tension is maintained.

➤ Take care to breathe evenly the entire time.

➤ Do not pull back the head in the neck. Look downward or slightly backward to the knees.

Back

The back has a differentiated system of muscles which start at the arches of the vertebrae and their spiny protrusions. The most important muscles are those in the lower back group *(Erector spinae)*, whose main functions are to keep the body erect and stabilize the spinal column. The *Erector spinae* consists of the entirety of the muscle package extending from the backbone. A middle section containing short muscles can be distinguished from an outer section with primarily long muscles. In addition, there are surface muscles such as the broad back muscle *(Latissimus)*, which also control the shoulder girdle and upper limbs.

A STRONG BACK IS A HEALTHY BACK

The training condition of the back muscles has a significant influence on health of the back. It can be assumed that about 80 percent of back complaints are associated with musculature that is either too weak or asymmetrically developed. It is therefore all the more important to ensure that training is varied and involves the smooth and uniform development of this muscle groups as a goal. Pay close attention to the correct movement technique, so that the sensitive structures of the spinal column, especially the disks, are protected as effectively as possible and are never subjected to excessive load or stress.

The back muscles: those in the top illustration are on the surface, while in the bottom illustration the underlying muscles are shown.

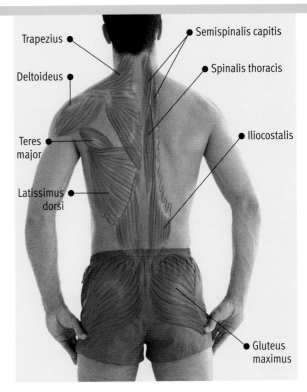

Trapezius
Deltoideus
Teres major
Latissimus dorsi
Semispinalis capitis
Spinalis thoracis
Iliocostalis
Gluteus maximus

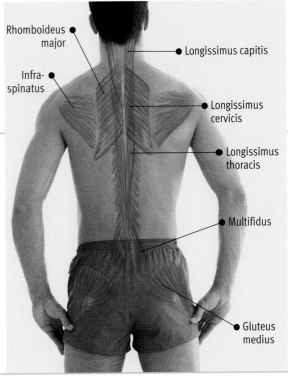

Rhomboideus major
Infra-spinatus
Longissimus capitis
Longissimus cervicis
Longissimus thoracis
Multifidus
Gluteus medius

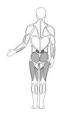

Lever back extension

MAIN MUSCLES:
lower back *(Erector spinae)*, depending on the variation, the lumbar or chest vertebrae area is emphasized.

SUPPORTING MUSCLES:
large buttock muscle *(Gluteus maximus)*, thigh biceps muscle *(Biceps femoris)*, semitendinosus, semimembranosus muscles

1. Starting position

Adjust the seat so that the axis of rotation of the machine is as far as possible an extension of the lumbar vertebrae. Ensure that the legs are stabilized at about hip width. In order to create a good pelvic position, the knees should be slightly bent (at about 20–30 degrees). Adjust the tread accordingly. The back padding should be positioned in the area of the shoulder blades in the basic exercise.

Exercise variations:

➤ Depending on the height of the machine's rotation axis selected, either the muscles around the lumbar vertebrae (with the axis at the level of the pelvic ridge) or in the area of the chest vertebrae (with the axis about 4 inches above the pelvic ridge) are more activated.

➤ A similar effect can be achieved by varying the height of the back padding (point of resistance), whereby the lower positioning accentuates the lumbar region and the higher position accentuates the chest vertebrae.

Evaluation

The lever back extension machine is part of the standard equipment of a modern training facility. The advantage of this machine is that the movement is partially prescribed. However if the exercise is performed incorrectly, it can cause an unbalanced load to be placed on the verte- brae. Nuances in the movement determine the training effectiveness.

Suitability:

Suitable for all levels of performance.

COORDINATION DEMANDS:
● ● ● ◐ ○

TRAINING EFFECTIVENESS:
● ● ● ● ◐

STRESS POTENTIAL:
● ● ● ◐ ○

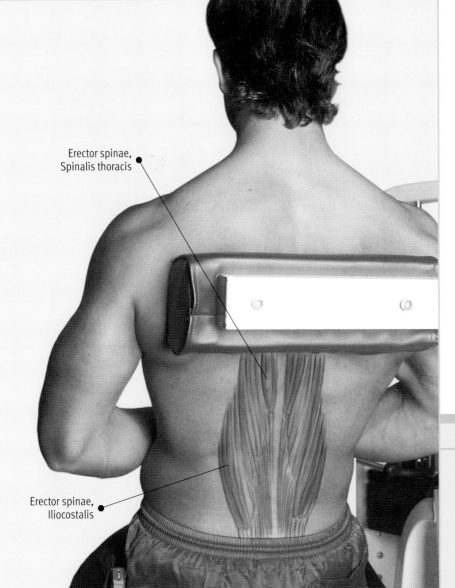

Erector spinae,
Spinalis thoracis

Erector spinae,
Iliocostalis

2. Movement

Actively flex the leg muscles to squeeze yourself into a sitting position. Start the exercise— depending on the training cond- ition and movement experience— with a slight to medium bend of the hips (about 30–40 degrees). The back can even be a little rounded in the starting postion, because that enhances the training effect of the individual short mus- cles between the vertebrae. Stretch your back until the spinal column is naturally erect (with lordosis). Maintain the tension in the mus- cles awhile returning to the start- ing position.

Important tips:

➤ Avoid compensatory movements in the pelvis.

➤ Always maintain an even rhythm.

➤ Beginners should start out with small movements, especially when bending forward.

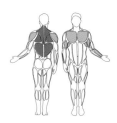

MAIN MUSCLES:
latissimus dorsi, lower trapezius *(Trapezius, P. asc.)*, rhomboids major *(Rhomboidei)*,teres major

SUPPORTING MUSCLES:
deltoid muscle *(Deltoideus)* posterior region *(Pars spinalis)*, upper chest muscle *(Pectoralis major)*, arm biceps muscle *(Biceps brachii)*, boxer's muscle *(Serratus anterior)*, flexing muscles of the forearm

Lateral pull-down

1. Starting position

Adjust the height of the seat so that the legs approach a right angle (knees bent at about 80 degrees). Tense up the trunk muscles and grab the handles far enough up so that the weights are a little raised when the arms are outstretched. The backs of the hands point out in the basic exercise. The back is straight and erect. Actively stabilize the shoulder girdle.

Exercise variation:

➤ Depending on the type of machine, the hands can grab further outwards with outward rotation in the shoulder joints, so that the *Latissimus* is more intensely activated. The backs of the hands then point toward the body.

Evaluation:
In contrast to the front pull-down, the movement here is determined by the machine.
Depending on the type of machine, the handles are pulled in straight or in circular paths of motion.

Suitability:
Recommended for beginners.

COORDINATION DEMANDS:
● ● ◐ ○ ○

TRAINING EFFECTIVENESS:
● ● ● ● ○

STRESS POTENTIAL:
● ◐ ○ ○ ○

eltoideus,
rs spinalis

eres major

imus dorsi

Trapezius,
ascendens

● Rhomboideus major   ● Biceps brachii

2. Movement

Pull on the handles with arms outstretched a few inches downward.
Then continue the movement with
increased bending of the elbow
joints, until the hands are roughly
at shoulder height. Now raise the
arms again while maintaining tension in the muscles, so that the
elbows do not fully extend.

Important tips:
➤ Perform the movement with deliberate force in the shoulder and back muscles.
➤ Always maintain the shoulders in a neutral position, that is, do not pull them up too high.
  Always look forward.

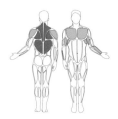

Front pull-down

MAIN MUSCLES:
latissimus dorsi, trapezius muscle *(Trapezius)*, lower fibers *(Pars ascendens)*, rhomboids major *(Rhomboidei)*, teres major

SUPPORTING MUSCLES:
deltoid muscle *(Deltoideus)*, upper chest muscle *(Pectoralis major)*, arm biceps muscle *(Biceps brachii)*, boxer's muscle *(Serratus anterior)*, flexing muscles of the forearm

1. Starting position

Adjust the height of the seat so that the legs are almost at right angles (knees at an angle of approximately 80 degrees). Grab the bar at about shoulder width enough so the arms can be fully extended. This enables you to fully use the entire movement and activate the *Latissimus*, the back should be slightly tilted forward. Hold the bar with a pronated or overgrip, with the backs of the hands pointing toward the body. Keep the legs in position with the padded bar. Begin the movement by tensing the back and shoulder blade muscles and slightly pulling back the shoulders.

Exercise variations:

➤ If your upper body is erect, you can place the bar just behind the head toward the neck instead of at chest height. This enhances the activity of the *Trapezius*. Slide forward on the seat far enough so that the movement can be performed vertically.

➤ As a rule, the higher up you grab the bar, the more the *Latissimus* is involved; the more closely together your hands are when they grab the bar, the more you activate the shoulder blades.

➤ The so-called supinated grip or undergrip—with the palms toward the body—allows you to involve the biceps more actively.

Evaluation:

The front pull-down is one of the favorite and most effective machine exercises and is standard equipment in every training facilty. Here again, the less the movement is guided by the machine, the more important the movement control.

Suitability:

For more advanced individuals. For beginners the conventional lateral pull-down machine is recommended (page 94).

COORDINATION DEMANDS:
● ● ● ○ ○

TRAINING EFFECTIVENESS:
● ● ● ● ◐

STRESS POTENTIAL:
● ● ● ○ ○

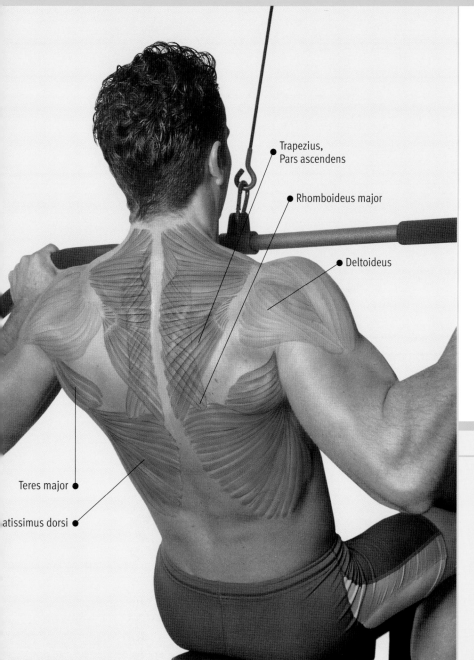

Trapezius, Pars ascendens

Rhomboideus major

Deltoideus

Teres major

atissimus dorsi

2. Movement

Pull the bar down a couple of inches at first, without moving the elbow joints. As the elbow bend increases, the elbows are then pulled down toward the chest. Now guide the bar back up while maintaining muscle tension. The elbows should not be fully extended in the final position.

Important tips:

➤ Do not hunch your shoulders because this can cause neck problems.

➤ It is better to reduce the weight and concentrate on the exercise.

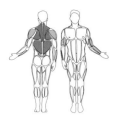

MAIN MUSCLES:
latissimus dorsi, trapezius muscle *(Trapezius),* lower fibers *(Pars ascendens),* rhomboids major *(Rhomboidei),* teres major

SUPPORTING MUSCLES:
deltoid muscle *(Deltoideus, P. spinalis),* arm biceps muscle *(Biceps brachii),* boxer's muscle *(Serratus anterior),* lower back *(Erector spinae)* in the region of the lumbar vertebrae, flexing muscles of the forearm

Lever seated row

1. Starting position

Adjust the seat position so that the legs are almost at right angles (knees at an angle of approximately 80 degrees). Stabilize the upper body on the chest pad—if the machine has one—and choose a grip from the basic exercise somewhat beneath shoulder level.

Exercise variations:

Depending on the position of the elbows and arms, you can activate different main muscle groups in a targeted way:

➤ In the basic exercise, use the vertical handles. The elbows move closely to the body, but are not raised. This is the best way in which to address the *Latissimus*.

➤ If you choose the horizontal handles, the elbows will be raised sideways, increasing the activity of the *Trapezius* and *Rhomboidei*. At the same time, the *Latissimus* is less involved.

Evaluation:

The lever seated row is one of the most important machines for the upper back, and particularly helpful to improve posture.

Suitability:

The machine provides good guidance, this exercise is recommended for all training levels.

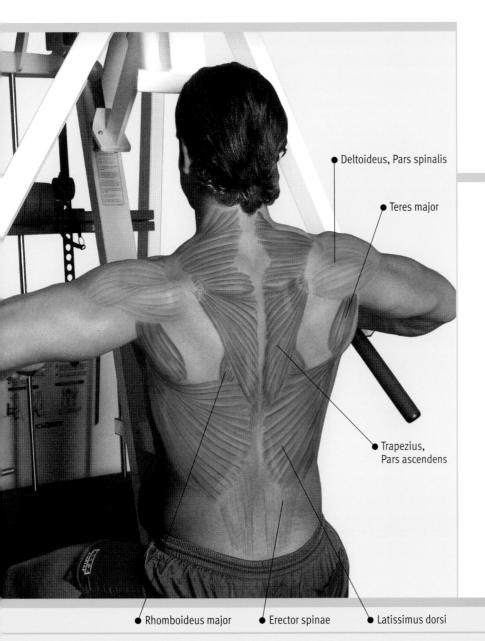

- Deltoideus, Pars spinalis
- Teres major
- Trapezius, Pars ascendens
- Rhomboideus major
- Erector spinae
- Latissimus dorsi

COORDINATION DEMANDS:

● ● ○ ○ ○

TRAINING EFFECTIVENESS:

● ● ● ● ◑

STRESS POTENTIAL:

● ● ◐ ○ ○

2. Movement

This movement, which is similar to that used in the lateral pull-down machine, is also started with the shoulder and back muscles in the lever seated row machine emphasizing the straightening the trunk. The first inches of the range of movement are performed with the arms still outstretched. Then bend the arms further and pull the handles far enough back, so that the elbows end up behind the shoulder axis. Always keep the back straight and look straight ahead.

Important tips:

➤ Always keep the back straight and avoid compensatory movements in the area of the lumbar and neck vertebrae.

➤ Stabilize yourself as much as possible and only use the chest pad when absolutely neccessary, for instance when using heavy weights or when the weight on the machine is greater than your own body weight.

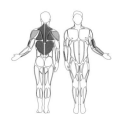

MAIN MUSCLES:
trapezius muscle *(Trapezius)*, especially the middle fibers *(Pars transversa)*, latissimus dorsi, rhomboids major*(Rhomboidei)*, arm biceps muscle *(Biceps brachii)*

SUPPORTING MUSCLES:
deltoid muscle *(Deltoideus)* posterior region *(Pars spinalis)*, flexing muscles of the forearm

One-arm short dumbbell row

1. Starting position

Position yourself as if on all fours, so that the body is supported on one side by the lower leg and by the outstretched arm on the bench. The other leg should be planted on the floor while the hand on that side is free. Keep the back in a straight line, and look downward. Grab the dumbbell with the free hand so that the back of the hand points outward.

Exercise variation:

➤ The pull toward the body is the best way to activate the *Latissimus*. If you spread the arm slightly and turn the dumbbell slightly inward—so the back of the hand is pointing forward—you will activate the *Trapezius* muscle more; the Latissimus will be less involved.

COORDINATION DEMANDS:
● ● ● ● ○

TRAINING EFFECTIVENESS:
● ● ● ◐ ○

STRESS POTENTIAL:
● ● ○ ○ ○

Evaluation:

This exercise requires clean movement technique.

Suitability:

Experience working with dumbbells is an advantage. For the more advanced muscle-trainer.

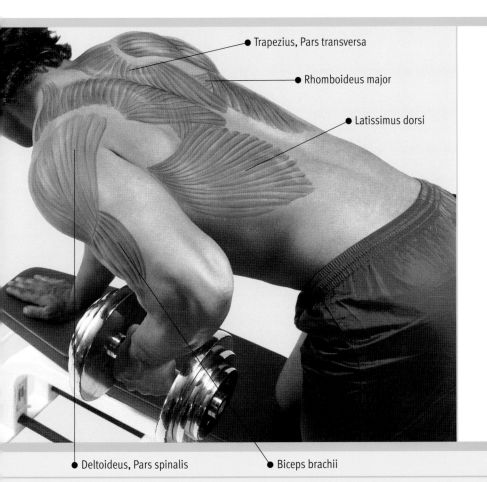

- Trapezius, Pars transversa
- Rhomboideus major
- Latissimus dorsi
- Deltoideus, Pars spinalis
- Biceps brachii

2. Movement

Leading with the elbow, pull the upper arm as far up as possible, without swinging it and without compensation, rotation, or sideways tilting in the back. Lift the weight uniformly in a vertical line. At the highest point, the elbow should be raised clearly above the back. Change sides.

Important tips:

➤ The exercise should be learned first using less weight for deliberate body control and stability of the back.

➤ Pay attention to the smooth and uniform development of the exercise, ensuring that both sides can manage the same load.

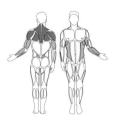

MAIN MUSCLES:
deltoid muscle *(Deltoideus, P. spin.)*, rhomboid muscles *(Rhomboidei)*, trapezius, muscle middle fibers *(Trapezius, P. transv.)*, teres minor, infra-spinatus/supraspinatus muscles

SUPPORTING MUSCLES:
lower back *(Erector spinae)*, internal/external oblique muscles *(Obliquus int./ext.)*, boxer's muscle *(Serratus ant.)*, arm triceps muscle *(Triceps brachii)*, forearm muscles

Trunk rotation with cable pull

1. Starting position

Fasten a handle to the lower pulley and position yourself sideways to the cable pull. Find a stable posture with the legs at about shoulder width and the knees lightly bent. Turn the upper body in the direction of the cable pull and lean slightly toward the handle. Grab the handle on the lower pulley so that the arm is bent at the elbow and the forearm turned slightly inward. The back of the hand should be pointed obliquely to the body.

Tense the trunk and shoulder muscles in order to stabilize the position. Always look toward the handle. Support the other arm by holding it bent on the side of your hip.

Evaluation:

Technically, a very demanding compound exercise that involves many muscles in the shoulder and back area. The trunk rotators are activated. The underlying muscles lend stability to the spinal column. The exercise should be performed under professional supervision and checked with a mirror.

Suitability:

Primarily for more advanced muscle-trainers with good coordination.

COORDINATION DEMANDS:
● ● ● ● ●

TRAINING EFFECTIVENESS:
● ● ● ● ◐

STRESS POTENTIAL:
● ● ● ● ○

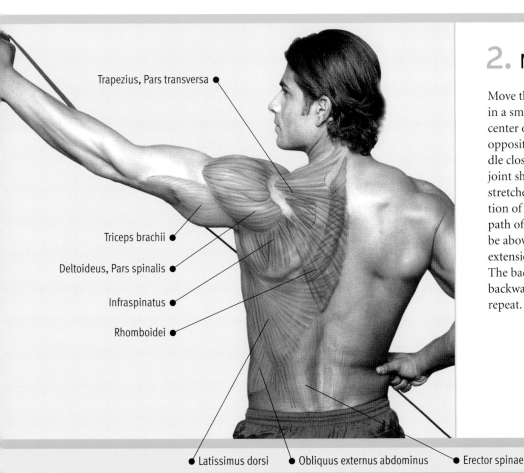

Trapezius, Pars transversa ●

Triceps brachii ●

Deltoideus, Pars spinalis ●

Infraspinatus ●

Rhomboidei ●

● Latissimus dorsi   ● Obliquus externus abdominus   ● Erector spinae

2. Movement

Move the hand from this position in a smooth movement past the center of the body and over to the opposite side. As you lead the handle close to the body, the elbow joint should become further stretched with the continuing rotation of the body. At the end of the path of movement, the arm should be above shoulder height in an extension of the rotation position. The back of the hand is pointing backward. Change sides and repeat.

Important tips:

➤ In all phases of the exercise, the gaze should be directed to the hand on the handle of the cable pull.

➤ The entire movement produces a rotation in the shoulder axis of about 90 degrees. The forearm is rotated from being turned inward (pronation) to being turned outward (supination).

➤ Make sure to guide the handle close to the body from the starting position and extend the arm only during the last third of the movement, or else the elbow will become overloaded.

➤ Clean movement technique has priority and if need be, you can reduce the weight to achieve it.

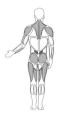

MAIN MUSCLES:
lower back *(Erector spinae)*

SUPPORTING MUSCLES:
large buttock muscle *(Gluteus maximus)*,
thigh biceps muscle *(Biceps femoris)*,
semitendinosus, semimembranosus muscles,
trapezius muscle *(Trapezius*, especially middle
fibers *Pars transversa)*, rhomboids muscle
(Rhomboidei), deltoid muscle
(Deltoideus, Pars spinalis)

Lumbar trainer

1. Starting position

Adjust the knee padding so that
the pelvis is covered to the pelvic
ridge. In order to better support
the lumbar vertebrae, the knee
padding can be placed somewhat
lower. Position the tread so that the
thigh is pressed to the padding by
the pressure of the soles of your
feet. In the basic position, the
hands should lie loosely behind the
head.

Exercise variations:

➤ Experienced athletes can roll the upper body up and down vertebra by vertebra. The rolling up begins
with the lumbar vertebrae, ending with the neck area of the spine. Rolling back proceeds in reverse,
beginning with the same neck area of the spine. The advantage of the rolling movement is that it focuses
on the short muscles between the vertebra.

➤ Instead of laying the hands on the head, the arms can be lifted to the sides, combined with an outward
rotation in the shoulder joint. In this way, additional muscles attached to the shoulder blades, especially
the rhomboid muscles, are activated. These are especially important for keeping the thoracic spine erect.

Evaluation:

The great advantage of this machine lies in the fact that the back muscles can be targeted for training and the back optimally secured with the padding at the same time. When the pelvis is fully supported, the machine is suitable for almost all performance levels. The position of the arms can be varied in the training.

Suitability:

For all target groups.

COORDINATION DEMANDS:
● ● ◐ ○ ○

TRAINING EFFECTIVENESS:
● ● ● ● ◐

STRESS POTENTIAL:
● ● ● ○ ○

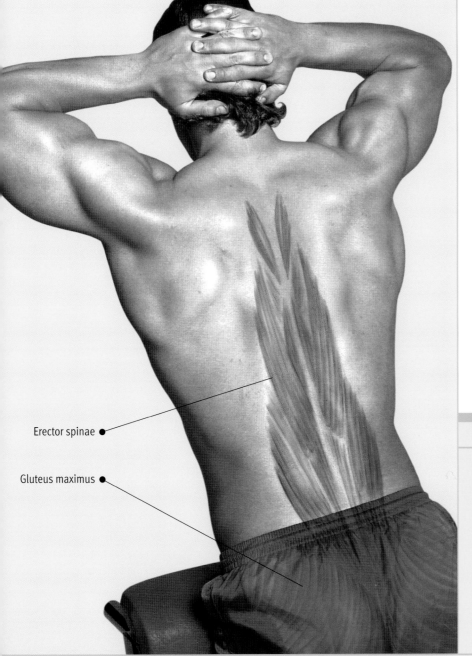

Erector spinae ●

Gluteus maximus ●

2. Movement

Start the exercise by rolling the back forward over the padding. Make sure the pelvis is stabilized by applying pressure with the soles of the feet on the tread. Then slowly straighten up the trunk until the back displays its normal amount of curve in the region of the lumbar vertebrae (lordosis). The head should always be lined up as an extension of the back. The gaze should be directed to the floor.

Important tips:

➤ Beginners should support the lumbar vertebrae with the padding and only train with minimal intensity. As training progresses, the padding can be positioned so that only pelvic ridge is still supported.

COORDINATION DEMANDS:
● ● ○ ○ ○

TRAINING EFFECTIVENESS:
● ● ● ◐ ○

STRESS POTENTIAL:
● ● ● ○ ○

MAIN MUSCLES:
large buttock muscle *(Gluteus maximus)*, lower back *(Erector spinae)* in the region of the lumbar vertebrae

SUPPORTING MUSCLES:
thigh biceps muscle *(Biceps femoris)*, semi-tendinosus, semimembranosus muscles

Backward leg lift with bench

Evaluation

In contrast to the floor exercises on the stomach, the advantage of this exercise is that the trunk and pelvis can be better stabilized to counteract overloading of the back.

Suitability:

For all target groups.

● Erector spinae, Iliocostalis

● Gluteus maximus

● Semitendinosus

● Semimembranosus

● Biceps femoris

Starting position and movement

Lie on the stomach on a bench, with the surface of the bench flush with the ridge of the pelvis. Stabilize the hands next to the body. Keep the head in an extension of the back and look downward. One leg is placed kneeling next to the bench. The other leg is stretched out backward with the foot pulled back. Now actively tense the trunk muscles. Guide the outstretched leg upward, leading with the heel—the tips of the toes should be slightly pulled in—until the leg is in line with the back. Hold the position at the point of reversal and, maintaining muscle tension, guide the leg back to a point just above the floor. Change sides and repeat the exercise.

Exercise variation:

➤ More advanced individuals can perform the exercise using both legs simultaneously or in continuous alternation (bicycle fashion).

Important tips:

➤ Always perform the movement smoothly, without any swing. The leg should not be lifted too high (being careful not to hollow the back).

➤ Breathe evenly while performing the exercise.

Chest

The most important of the chest muscles as far as fitness training is concerned is the large pectoral muscle *(Pectoralis major)*, while the small pectoral muscle *(Pectoralis minor)* plays a subordinate role. The large chest muscles have three regions and form the front of the armpit. It consists of the upper *(Pars clavicularis)*, transverse *(Pars sternocostalis)* and lower *(Pars abdominalis)* fibers. Well developed chest muscles give the chest a rounded contour, which is often an important training goal for men.

The chest muscles cover and stabilize the shoulder joint from the front like a cap and are involved in movements of this joint. They are responsible for the pulling in (adduction), forward lifting (anteversion), and the inward rotation of the arm. The chest muscles have a special meaning for many types of sports, if for example an acceleration of the arm with respect to the trunk is required, as it is with throwing or swimming.

OPTIMAL JOINT BALANCE IS CRUCIAL

People who intensively train the chest muscles should combine the training with targeted exercises in the area of the back and shoulder blades, exercising the *Latissimus* and *Rhomboids,* for instance. If this is not done, a muscle imbalance will pull the shoulders forward, a problem which affects many athletes and fitness fanatics. Targeted stretch exercises for the chest muscles help to maintain the optimal joint balance.

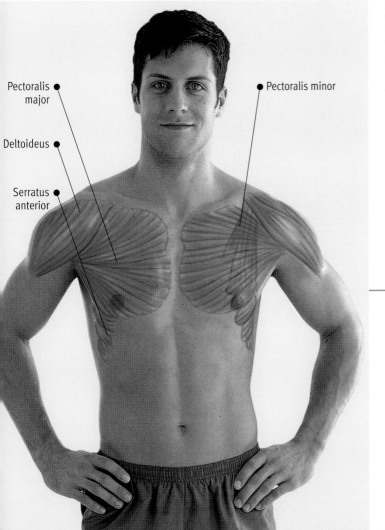

Pectoralis major

Pectoralis minor

Deltoideus

Serratus anterior

The chest muscles—in fitness training, the *Pectoralis major* plays a central role.

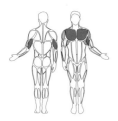

MAIN MUSCLES:
large pectoral muscle *(Pectoralis major)*, arm triceps muscle *(Triceps brachii)*

SUPPORTING MUSCLES:
deltoid muscle *(Deltoideus)* anterior region *(Pars clavicularis)*, boxer's muscle *(Serratus anterior)*

Lever inclined chest press

1. Starting position

Adjust the seat and handles so that the hands are positioned a little below the shoulder level. The back should be in complete contact with the back of the seat. Grab the handles symmetrically and firmly (do not bend down the hands, keep the wrist level). The elbows should be bent and pointing outward. Tense the trunk muscles before starting the movement in order to actively stabilize the position.

Exercise variations:

➤ A wide grip position enhances the effect on the chest muscles.

➤ With double-hinged machines, the arms can be guided together in a forward movement, which also enhances the training of the chest muscles.

➤ On some machines, the arms can be moved one at a time (decoupled resistance adjustment). This makes greater demands on movement coordination and ensures that both arms are uniformly trained.

Evaluation:

A simple, effective exercise for strengthening the chest muscles, with especially high stimulation for the anterior region of the Deltoids. The chest press is not as effective as the bench press (page 112), but the exercise is considered by many people to be more comfortable as a sitting exercise.

Suitability:

Especially good for beginners.

COORDINATION DEMANDS:
● ◐ ○ ○ ○

TRAINING EFFECTIVENESS:
● ● ● ◐ ○

STRESS POTENTIAL:
● ◐ ○ ○ ○

Deltoideus

Pectoralis major

Serratus anterior

Triceps brachii

2. Movement

Move the handles evenly forward, until the elbows are almost though not completely extended. Then bring back the arms against the pressure of the machine, until the upper arms are in a line with the shoulder axis.

Important tips:

➤ Do not move the elbows too far behind the shoulder axis, which can lead to overloading the front shoulder joint structures.

➤ Ensure during the entire movement that the hands are stable and in line with the forearms.

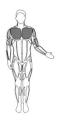

MAIN MUSCLES:
large pectoral muscle *(Pectoralis major)*

SUPPORTING MUSCLES:
deltoid muscle *(Deltoideus)* anterior region
(Pars clavicularis), arm biceps muscle *(Biceps
brachii)* short head *(Caput breve)*

Butterfly

1. Starting position

Adjust the seat so that the knee is
bent at slightly less than a right
angle (about 80 degrees). Position
the upper arms more or less parallel to the height of the shoulders.
The elbows in the basic exercise
should be bent at right angles and
the hands pointing upward (outward rotation in the shoulder
joint). If the machine has entry
supports, use these to guide you;
the movement arms are guided
with a foot pedal. Move the lever
arms far enough outward so that
the upper arms form a line with
the shoulder axis. Tense the trunk
muscles to stabilize and maintain
the body posture.

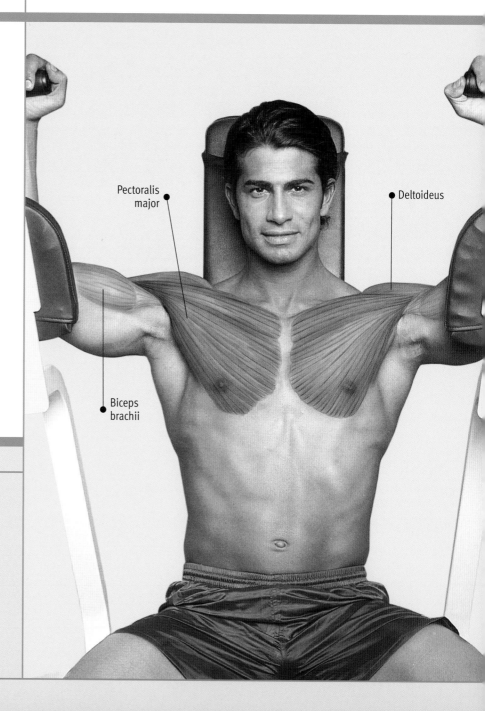

Pectoralis major

Deltoideus

Biceps brachii

Exercise variation:

➤ Depending on the machine type,
the exercise also be performed
without outward rotation in the
shoulder joint. This increases the
activity of the upper chest muscle
region. The forearms should be
parallel and almost at right angles
to the upper arms with the hands
pointing forward.

Evaluation:

The butterfly is considered an outstanding exercise for targeted chest muscle training. The advantage of the machine is that it guides the movement and the holding of the body in position which means that it is suitable for high-resistance training.

Suitability:

Suitable for every level of ability.

COORDINATION DEMANDS:
● ○ ○ ○ ○

TRAINING EFFECTIVENESS:
● ● ● ● ○

STRESS POTENTIAL:
● ● ◐ ○ ○

2. Movement

Squeeze the padding evenly together, using the chest muscles. The lever arms should be brought far forward but should not touch at the end of the movement. Concentrate on bringing back the arms slowly so that the upper arms are in line with the shoulder axis.

Important tips:

➤ The arms should not be moved too far behind the shoulder level. This position does not create any additional effects for the chest muscles and substantially increases the load on the shoulder joints.

➤ Avoid emphasizing the arms to support the movement because that reduces the effect on the chest muscles and leads to compensatory movements.

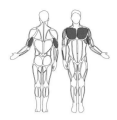

MAIN MUSCLES:
large pectoral muscle *(Pectoralis major)*, arm triceps muscle *(Triceps brachii)*

SUPPORTING MUSCLES:
deltoid muscle *(Deltoideus)*, especially the anterior region *(Pars clavicularis)*, boxer's muscle *(Serratus anterior)*

Bench press with barbell

1. Starting position

Lie on your back on a weight bench, and lift and bend the legs or position them on the floor at the lower end of the bench. This helps counteract a hollow back. The knees should be bent almost at right angles to the surface of the bench. Grab the barbell with wrists fixed at a slightly greater width than the shoulders and tense the trunk muscles.
Now bring down barbell in a controlled fashion in the direction of the breast bone, but do not rest the barbell on the chest.

Exercise variations:

➤ A wide grip position enhances the effect on the chest muscles.

➤ Machine bench presses are not as effective as training with free weights, such as these, because the optimal, lightly swinging movement is suppressed by the machine. The more experienced should therefore train with free weights.

Evaluation:

Bench presses are fitness exercise classics.

Suitability:

The use of free weights require some training experience. If the barbell is supported by a guide on the sides by a machine and the right weights are used, the exercise can also be performed by less experienced trainers.

COORDINATION DEMANDS:
● ● ● ◐ ○

TRAINING EFFECTIVENESS:
● ● ● ● ●

STRESS POTENTIAL:
● ● ● ● ○

● Deltoideus

● Pectoralis major

● Serratus anterior   ● Triceps brachii

2. Movement

Press the barbell in a uniform movement upward, until the elbows are almost but not completely extended. This enables you to maintain the muscle tension at the height of the movement. Then let down the barbell slowly and evenly, until the upper arms form a line with the plane of the shoulders.

Important tips:

➤ Avoid letting down the barbell too far. This happens if the upper arms are clearly below the plane of the shoulders, or even rest on the breast bone. These positions are ineffectual in exercising the chest muscles and substantially increase the load on the shoulder joints.

MAIN MUSCLES:
large pectoral muscle *(Pectoralis major)*

SUPPORTING MUSCLES:
deltoid muscle *(Deltoideus)*, especially anterior region *(Pars clavicularis)*, boxer's muscle *(Serratus anterior)*, arm biceps muscle *(Biceps brachii)*

Dumbbell fly

1. Starting position

Lie on your back on a flat or slightly slanted bench. The knees should be bent almost at right angles, so that the palms lie flat. Grab the dumbbells and keep the wrists firm but do not stretch out the arms completely over the shoulders (see photo, page 115). The backs of the hands point outward. Tense the trunk muscles to stabilize the exercise.

Exercise variation:

➤ The exercise can be performed on a slanted bench. The greater angle of slant enhances the activity of the anterior region of the deltoid muscles, while the effect on the chest muscles is lessened.

Evaluation:

In contrast to exercises with the barbell, in this exercise both arms and both sides of the body are trained uniformly.

Suitability:

The exercise is only recommended for experienced athletes, because it can easily cause overloading.

COORDINATION DEMANDS:
● ● ● ● ○

TRAINING EFFECTIVENESS:
● ● ● ◐ ○

STRESS POTENTIAL:
● ● ● ◐ ○

ceps brachii ●

Deltoideus ●

● Pectoralis major ● Serratus anterior

2. Movement

Let the slightly bent arms slowly sink to the sides, until the elbows are just below the shoulder axis. Guide the arms upward from this position, leaving the angle in the elbow joints unchanged, and without letting the dumbbells touch at the highest point.

Important tips:

➤ Avoid letting the dumbbells sink too low. When the upper arms drop below shoulder level, you put a strain on the shoulder joints, and there are no significant additional benefits for the chest muscles.

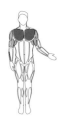

Cable standing fly

MAIN MUSCLES:
large pectoral muscle *(Pectoralis major)*

SUPPORTING MUSCLES:
deltoid muscle *(Deltoideus)*, especially
anterior region *(Pars clavicularis)*,
boxer's muscle *(Serratus anterior)*,
arm biceps muscle *(Biceps brachii)*,
pectoralis minor muscle

1. Starting position

Position yourself between, slightly
in front, of the two blocks of a
double cable-pull. Take a small
step, leaning slightly forward at the
trunk. Grab the handles on both
sides on the high pulley of the
cable pull. The arms should be
close to the body in an extension of
the shoulder axis and slightly bent.
Stabilize the body by tensing the
trunk muscles.

Exercise variation:

➤ The higher the arms are raised to perform the movement, the greater the effect on all areas of the large
chest muscles *(Pars clavicularis, sternocostalis,* and *abdominalis)*.

Evaluation:

This exercise using the double cable-pull trains all areas of the large chest muscles. To perform correctly and symmetrically, the movement requires very good body control.

Suitability:

For experienced athletes.

COORDINATION DEMANDS:
● ● ● ● ○

TRAINING EFFECTIVENESS:
● ● ● ● ◐

STRESS POTENTIAL:
● ● ● ◐ ○

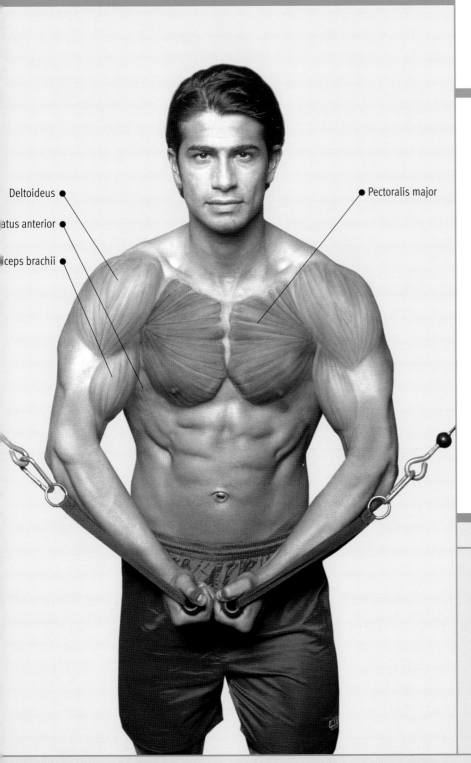

Deltoideus

atus anterior

ceps brachii

Pectoralis major

2. Movement

Press the handles in an arching movement in front of the body, at roughly pelvis level. The handles should not touch each other. Hold them together briefly, then bring back the arms in the same path of movement against the pull of the cable to the starting position, until the hands are next to the body in an extension of the shoulder axis.

Important tips:

➤ Do not fully extend the elbows.
➤ Keep the wrists stable behind the handles and do not let them drop down at any point.
➤ If possible, perform the exercise while checking in the mirror.

COORDINATION DEMANDS:
● ● ● ○ ○

TRAINING EFFECTIVENESS:
● ● ● ◐ ○

STRESS POTENTIAL:
● ● ◐ ○ ○

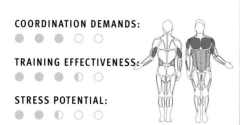

MAIN MUSCLES:
large pectoral muscle *(Pectoralis major)*, deltoid muscle *(Deltoideus)* anterior region *(Pars acromialis)*, arm triceps muscle *(Triceps brachii)*

SUPPORTING MUSCLES:
boxer's muscle *(Serratus anterior)*, entire abdominal musculature (for stabilization)

Kneeling push-up

Evaluation:
A classic fitness exercise without a machine for chest and shoulder areas.

Suitability:
Because of the many possibilities for variation in individual performance, the pushup is suitable for all target groups. This version performed on the knees is recommended for beginners because it is not as strenuous as the completely extended pushup.

● Pectoralis major
● Deltoideus
● Triceps brachii
● Rectus abdominis

Starting position and movement

Go into the pushup position with your legs slightly bent. In this version the legs are folded back over the knees. Plant the hands at somewhat more than shoulder width, parallel to the body. The tips of the fingers should point forward. Actively tense the abdominal and buttock muscles in order to stabilize the trunk and guard against a hollow back. The back should be straight and the head should be in line with the back. Now drop down the trunk in a controlled fashion by increasingly bending the elbows until the chin is about 2 inches from the floor. Then press the body back up, without swinging it, until the elbows are almost straight.

Exercise variations:
➤ In order to increase the level of difficulty, you can perform the pushups with outstretched legs. In this version the trunk should be in line with the outstretched legs.

➤ The further apart you place the hands, the more the chest muscles are worked, while the closer together they are, the more you stimulate the triceps.

Important tips:
➤ Ensure that the hands are not turned in or out. This does not add any benefit to your training and overloads the joints.

Shoulders

The shoulder area is crisscrossed with a number of muscles that stabilize the joint system and the arms with respect to the trunk in all planes of movement. Each shoulder movement consists of a combination of individual movements that are distributed among the various joints. The starting point for the arm movements is in the shoulder joint formed by the shoulder ball and the shoulder blade socket. The joint is sheathed in muscles.

THE PROTECTION OF TRAINED MUSCLES

The complete range of motion in the shoulder area is very large. Since the joint system is only lightly secured by the bones and ligament structures, a high level of training of the surrounding muscles is particularly important.

For the sake of simplification, some of the muscle groups are listed in the exercise section. For instance, under the catchall description "supporting shoulder blade muscles", the following muscles are listed:

➤ trapezius muscle
➤ rhomboid muscles *(Rhomboidei)*
➤ levator scapulae
➤ small pectoral muscle *(Pectoralis minor)*
➤ boxer's muscle *(Serratus anterior)*

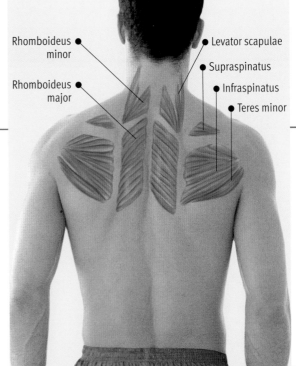

Trapezius

Latissimus dorsi

Teres major

Deltoideus

Rhomboideus minor

Rhomboideus major

Levator scapulae

Supraspinatus

Infraspinatus

Teres minor

The neck and shoulder muscles – the illustration above shows the surface muscles, the picture shows the underlying muscles.

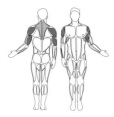

Lever shoulder press

MAIN MUSCLES:
deltoid muscle *(Deltoideus)* upper and anterior region *(Pars clavicularis* and *acromialis)*, arm triceps muscle *(Triceps brachii)*

SUPPORTING MUSCLES:
trapezius muscles *(Trapezius)* upper fibers *(Pars descendens)*, boxer's muscle *(Serratus anterior)*, according to the angle of tilt of the seat back, large pectoral muscle *(Pectoralis major)*

1. Starting position

Make sure the seat is secure with your legs slightly spread and bent at the knees at a little less than right angles (about 80 degrees). The back should be in complete in contact with seat back. Hold the handles at shoulder height or slightly below (without compensatory movement of the trunk). Straighten the upper body and actively tense the trunk muscles.

Exercises variations:

➤ In the basic exercise, hold the handles in front of the shoulders in a neutral position with the backs of the hands pointing outward. Depending on the type of machine, as a variation you can also use another handle position with outward rotation in the shoulder joints. The backs of the hands will then point backward.

➤ The steeper the back of the seat, the greater the intensity for the shoulder muscles; the flatter you are against the seat back, the more the chest muscles are brought into play.

Evaluation:

An effective basic machine exercise for the compound training of the shoulder and arm muscles.

Suitability:

The guided movement is easy to master and is therefore suitable for all target groups.

● Deltoideus

eps brachii ●

ralis major ●

● Serratus anterior

2. Movement

Press the handles in a uniform movement upward, until the arms are almost (but not completely) outstretched. Hold this position briefly, then slowly guide the arms back against the weight to the starting position.

Important tips:

➤ The shoulders always stay in a stable, neutral position (there should be no compensation upward or forward).

➤ If problems arise with over-the-head exercises, use the handle position in front of the body. It is also a good idea to limit the movement range.

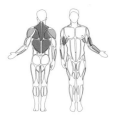

MAIN MUSCLES:
latissimus dorsi *(Latissimus dorsi)*, trapezius muscle *(Trapezius*, especially *Pars ascendens)*, teres major, arm biceps muscle *(Biceps brachii)*

SUPPORTING MUSCLES:
deltoid muscle *(Deltoideus)* posterior region *(Pars spinalis)*, rhomboid muscles *(Rhomboidei)*, boxer's muscle *(Serratus anterior)*, flexing muscles of the forearms

Assisted pull-up

1. Starting position

Step onto the tread or—depending on the machine type—kneel on the leg padding. Grab the handles at slightly wider than shoulder width, with the backs of the hands pointing toward the body (overhand). Tense the shoulder and neck muscles deliberately so that the shoulders are pulled down. The head should form an extension of the back and the gaze should be directed forward.

Exercises variations:

➤ The wider apart you hold the handles, the greater the activity of the *Latissimus.*

➤ If you want to additionally emphasize the biceps muscle, then the so-called underhand grip is recommended. In this position the palms, rather than the backs of the hands, point toward the body.

Evaluation:

This is an outstanding complex exercise for several large muscle groups. With the aid of the standing or kneeling platform the intensity can be regulated and the exercise made easy enough so that pull-ups can be performed by people of all ability levels.

Suitability:

At appropriate levels of intensity, the exercise is suitable for all levels of ability.

COORDINATION DEMANDS:
● ◑ ○ ○ ○

TRAINING EFFECTIVENESS:
● ● ● ● ○

STRESS POTENTIAL:
● ◑ ○ ○ ○

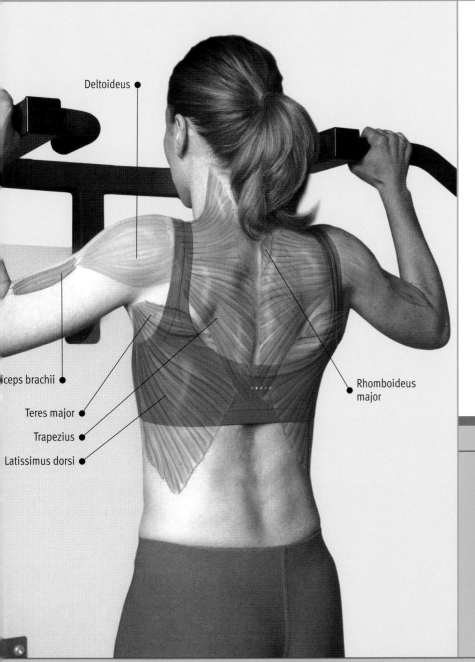

Deltoideus

Biceps brachii

Teres major

Trapezius

Latissimus dorsi

Rhomboideus major

2. Movement

Pull yourself up in a uniform motion until your head is at least as high as your hands. Then let the body drop down slowly to the starting position, in which the elbows are still slightly bent at the lowest point. This helps maintain muscle tension throughout the exercise.

Important tips:

➤ The back should be as relaxed as possible throughout the movement.

➤ Ensure that the shoulders are actively stabilized and are not pulled up at the beginning of the movement.

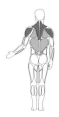

Reverse butterfly

MAIN MUSCLES:
rhomboid muscles *(Rhomboidei)*, trapezius muscle *(Trapezius)*, especially middle and lower fibers *(Pars transversa* and *ascendens)*, deltoid muscle *(Deltoideus, Pars spinalis)*

SUPPORTING MUSCLES:
teres minor *(Teres minor)*, infraspinatus muscle, latissimus dorsi *(Latissimus dorsi)*, lower back muscle *(Erector spinae)*

1. Starting position

Adjust the seat so that the knees are bent almost at right angles (about 80 degrees). Straighten the upper body and tense the trunk muscles for stability. Now position the arms at shoulder height or slightly below it. Depending on the equipment or type of machine, the arms should be in a horizontal or vertical position (as shown here, with outward rotation in the shoulder joint). Consciously tense the muscles between the shoulder blades.

Exercise variations:

➤ The higher the position of the arms, the greater the effect on the shoulder blade holding muscles. The lower the arms, the greater the effect on the *Latissimus*.

➤ With some machines the lever arms can only be moved with the hands and there are no pads on which to rest the elbows. The movement is distributed among the wrist and elbow and shoulder joints (multi-joint training). In this variation, take extra care to ensure that the shoulder muscles are responsible for the movement and do not rely on the strength of the arms.

Evaluation:

An important exercise for the muscles that are allow for an erect posture of the upper body. For those who sit a lot, it is a good compensation exercise.

Suitability:

With the right weight good for all levels.

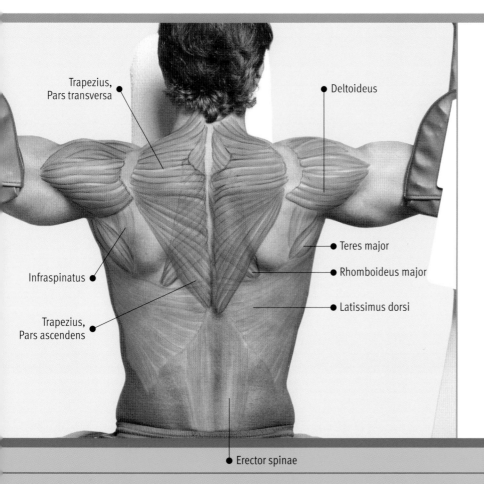

Trapezius, Pars transversa

Deltoideus

Infraspinatus

Trapezius, Pars ascendens

Teres major

Rhomboideus major

Latissimus dorsi

Erector spinae

2. Movement

Push back the lever arms of the machine slowly and evenly, using pressure from the upper arms, right to the shoulder axis or a little beyond (single joint version). At the point of reversal, hold the position, then bring back the arms against the pressure of the machine without letting the lever arms touch each other.

Important tips:

➤ Train with small weights at first ensuring your technique is absolutely clean.

➤ Be sure to avoid compensatory movements in the area of the neck or else strain can occur. Position the arms below the shoulders at first and gradually increase the angle upward.

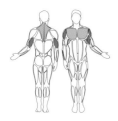

MAIN MUSCLES:
deltoid muscle *(Deltoideus)* upper and anterior region *(Pars clavicularis* and *acromialis)*, arm triceps muscle *(Triceps brachii)*

SUPPORTING MUSCLES:
trapezius muscle *(Trapezius)* upper fibers *(Pars descendens)*, boxer's muscle *(Serratus anterior)*, according to the tilt angle of the seat back, large pectoral muscle *(Pectoralis major)*

Neck press with dumbbells

1. Starting position

Adjust the bench so that you can sit firmly and comfortably with your legs slightly spread. The seat back should be slightly tipped back and your back should be in complete contact with the padding. Bring the arms to shoulder height at more-or-less a right angle, grip the dumbbells and steady your wrists, with the palms pointing forward. Tense the trunk muscles and straighten the upper body.

Pectoralis major

Deltoideus

Triceps brachii

Serratus anterior

Exercise variations:

➤ The steeper the angle of the seat back, the greater the effect will be on the upper anterior region of the deltoid muscles. The more upright the seat back, the more the chest muscles are stimulated.

➤ You can vary the exercise so that the dumbbells are at 90 degrees when they are at their highest point. The backs of the hands should be pointing outward in the final position.
In this variation, the effect on the inner fibers of the chest muscles is intensified.

Evaluation:

A basic exercise for the compound training of the shoulder and arm muscles.

Suitability:

With the appropriate weight and use of the mirror for checking performance, suitable for all levels.

COORDINATION DEMANDS:
● ● ● ○ ○

TRAINING EFFECTIVENESS:
● ● ● ● ○

STRESS POTENTIAL:
● ● ● ○ ○

2. Movement

Press the dumbbells upward in a smooth, steady movement until the arms are almost—but not completely— extended. Hold this position briefly, and then move the arms back to the starting position, so that the dumbbells are at about shoulder height.

Important tips:

➤ The shoulders remain in a stable neutral position during the entire movement (no compensation upward or forward).

➤ Anyone who has a problem with training in the over-the-head area should start with the seat back tilted backward and limit the range of movement.

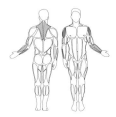

MAIN MUSCLES:
deltoid muscle *(Deltoideus)* upper and anterior region *(Pars clavicularis* and *acromialis)*

SUPPORTING MUSCLES:
trapezius muscle *(Trapezius)* upper and lower fibers *(Pars descendens* and *ascendens)*, supraspinatus muscle, forearm muscles

Lateral raise with dumbbells

1. Starting position

Get into a stable upright position, either with the legs slightly apart or with the feet spread at hip width. The knee joints are slightly bent. Actively tense the back muscles and hold the dumbbells with the upper arms facing the body and the elbows bent. The hands should be slightly turned in, while the backs of the hands point outward in the starting position. Stabilize this basic position by tensing the trunk and shoulder muscles.

Exercise variations:

➤ Since the exercise is primarily effective in the last third of the movement, you can intensify it by performing a few repetitions in this area (end contractions).

➤ The exercise can also be performed in a sitting position.

Evaluation:

A basic exercise for strengthening the shoulder muscles. Beginners should only train with bent elbows (short leverage) and light to medium weights.

Suitability:

Suitable for all ability levels.

COORDINATION DEMANDS:
● ● ● ◑ ○

TRAINING EFFECTIVENESS:
● ● ● ● ○

STRESS POTENTIAL:
● ● ● ○ ○

Deltoideus, pars acromialis

Deltoideus, Pars clavicularis

2. Movement

Guide the dumbbells on both sides in a uniform movement to about shoulder height. The elbows should be in line with the shoulder axis in the final position. The backs of the hands point upward and can be turned slightly inward. Return the dumbbells slowly and symmetrically to the starting position. The arms should never be allowed to rest against the trunk (maintain muscle tension).

Important tips:

➤ The shoulders remain in a stable neutral position during the entire movement (no compensation upward or to the front).

➤ The most frequent mistake is using weights that are too heavy.

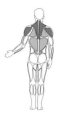

Reverse fly with dumbbells

MAIN MUSCLES:
rhomboid muscles *(Rhomboidei)*, trapezius muscle *(Trapezius)*, especially the middle and anterior region *(Pars transversa* and *descendens)*, deltoid muscle *(Deltoideus, Pars spinalis)*

SUPPORTING MUSCLES:
teres minor *(Teres minor)*, infraspinatus muscle, latissimus dorsi, lower back muscle *(Erector spinae)*

1. Starting position

Lie on your stomach on a flat or slightly tilted bench. The head should be kept free in an extension of the back, and the gaze directed downward. Place the feet at each side, with the knees bent, in order to stabilize the position. Hold the dumbbells directly beneath the shoulder axis. The elbows should be slightly bent, with the backs of the hands pointing forward.

Exercise variations:

➤ This exercise is easier if you use a somewhat tilted bench instead of a flat one. The rule is, the more tilted the bench, the less the intensity.

➤ You can turn the dumbbells slightly inward in order to increase the intensity.

➤ The exercise can be performed very effectively with barbells underneath the flat bench.

Evaluation:

The back is held securely in place with this exercise. It is effective training for the shoulder and neck muscles.

Suitability:

In comparison with exercising on machines, this exercise is more demanding from the standpoint of coordination and is therefore recommended primarily for advanced trainers.

COORDINATION DEMANDS:
● ● ● ◐ ○

TRAINING EFFECTIVENESS:
● ● ● ● ◐

STRESS POTENTIAL:
● ● ● ○ ○

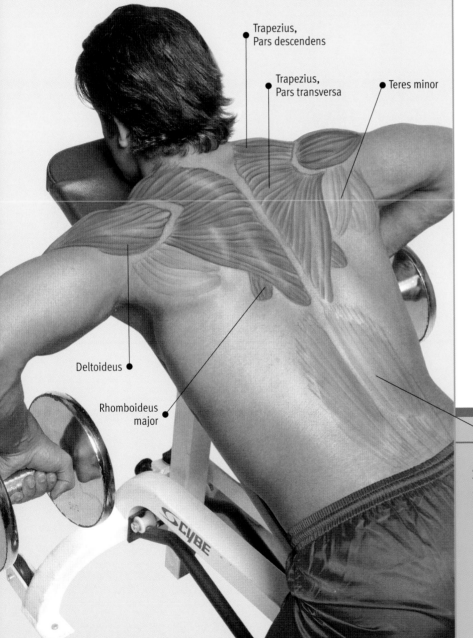

Trapezius, Pars descendens

Trapezius, Pars transversa

Teres minor

Deltoideus

Rhomboideus major

Erector spinae

2. Movement

Raise the arms with the elbows slowly and in a controlled fashion. Bring the shoulder blades as close together as possible as you come to the reversal point, and hold the movement briefly. Then lower the dumbbells back to the starting position while maintaining the muscle tension.

Important tips:

➤ Beginners should train at first with less weight and only move the elbows to about shoulder height.

➤ Always keep the head in line with the back and avoid any compensatory movement in the neck.

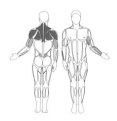

MAIN MUSCLES:
deltoid muscle *(Deltoideus, P. spin.)*, rhomboid muscles *(Rhomboidei)*, trapezius muscle *(Trapezius, especially P. desc. and P. asc.)*, teres minor *(Teres minor)*, infraspinatus muscle, supraspinatus muscle

SUPPORTING MUSCLES:
Lower back muscle *(Erector spinae)*, arm triceps muscle *(Triceps brachii)*, forearm muscles

Diagonal lateral cable raise

1. Starting position

Position yourself centrally between a double cable-pull and hold the handles on the lower pulley with your hands crossed. The backs of the hands should point downward. Bend your knees slightly and lean the otherwise straight upper body at an angle of about 30 degrees forward. The head should be in line with the back and, depending on the angle of the upper body, the gaze should be directed downward either diagonally or straight. Stabilize this position by tensing the trunk and shoulder muscles.

Exercise variations:

➤ Start with the upper body only slightly tilted forward. The greater the tilt of the upper body, the greater the training effect will be for the muscles between the shoulder blades.

➤ In order to further enhance the exercise, the arms can be raised slightly behind the plane of the shoulders in the end position, so that the shoulder blades are brought closer together.

Evaluation:

A technically demanding compound exercise for the countless muscles that are responsible for keeping the posture straight and erect. The exercise should be practiced at first under professional guidance and by checking in the mirror.

Suitability:

Most suitable for advanced athletes.

COORDINATION DEMANDS:
● ● ● ● ◐

TRAINING EFFECTIVENESS:
● ● ● ● ◐

STRESS POTENTIAL:
● ● ● ◐ ○

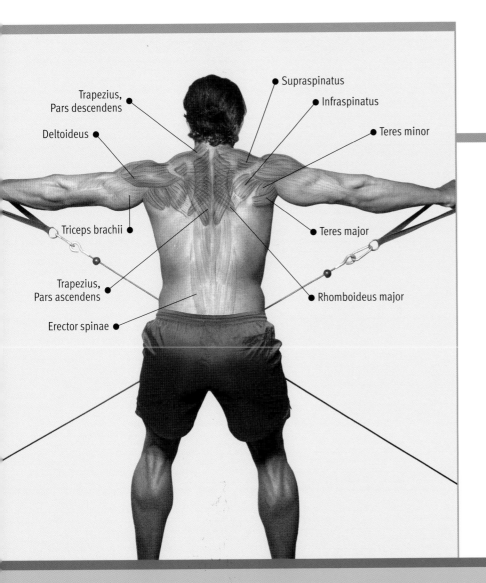

Supraspinatus
Infraspinatus
Teres minor
Trapezius, Pars descendens
Deltoideus
Triceps brachii
Teres major
Trapezius, Pars ascendens
Rhomboideus major
Erector spinae

2. Movement

Pull the handles from the crossed position close to the body, using a diagonal movement over the chest and outward. The arms, that are initially bent, should gradually stretch out to their fullest extent. In the final position, the arms should be in line with the shoulder axis, with the backs of the hands pointing upward at a slant. Hold this position briefly, then bring the handles back in reverse order to the starting position. Do not release the weights but do maintain tension in the muscles.

Important tips:

➤ In the starting position, the handles must be guided close to the body and in the last third of the movement the arms must be outstretched (otherwise the elbows will be overloaded).

➤ Clean movement technique is of prime importance, reduce the weight if need be.

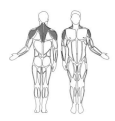

MAIN MUSCLES:
trapezius muscle *(Trapezius)*, especially the upper fibers *(Pars descendens)*, deltoid muscle *(Deltoideus)*

SUPPORTING MUSCLES:
rhomboid muscles *(Rhomboidei)*, levator scapulae

Upright cable row

1. Starting position

Attach a V-shaped handle or special rope to the lower pulley of a cable pull. This supports a neutral wrist position, that is, the wrists should be an extension of the forearms, without bending down. Adopt a stable stance with the feet at shoulder width in front of the cable machine. The knees should be slightly bent. Consciously tense the abdominals, buttocks, and back muscles for stability.

Exercise variations:

➤ Alternatively, you can train with dumbbells or barbells. In comparison with the exercise on the cable pull, the demand on coordination is greater if weights are used.

➤ The closer together you hold the cables and weights, the greater the effect is in the upper region of the trapezoid muscles.

Evaluation:

The exercise is especially good for training the upper region of the trapezius muscle. The execution is relatively simple.

Suitability:

For all levels of training. However beginners and persons with problems in the shoulder and neck area should exercise slowly and with small weights at first (to avoid neck strain).

COORDINATION DEMANDS:
● ● ○ ○ ○

TRAINING EFFECTIVENESS:
● ● ● ● ◐

STRESS POTENTIAL:
● ● ● ◐ ○

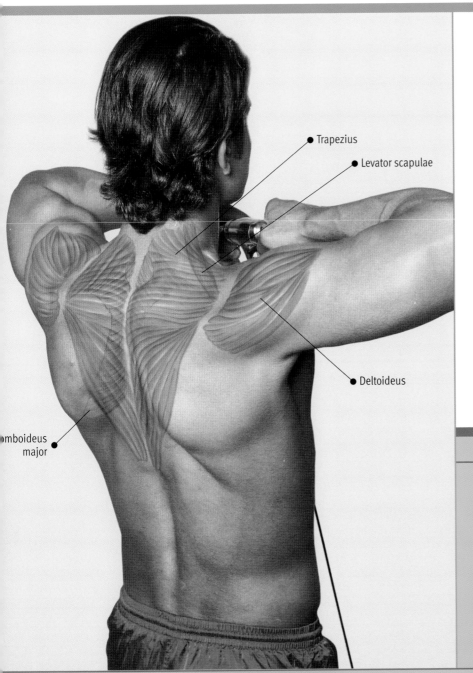

Trapezius

Levator scapulae

Deltoideus

mboideus major

2. Movement

The movement is performed with a narrow grip position (the hands should be right next to each other) in a straight line along the length of the body to just below the chin. The shoulders should be lifted straight up as high as possible. The elbows are parallel and point outward. Hold the highest position briefly and then guide the handles back against the braking action of the cable to the starting position, keeping the arms outstretched.

Important tips:

➤ Emphasize controlled pulling and avoid swinging movements, especially at the beginning and end.

➤ Avoid compensatory movements in the area of the neck. Stretch the neck muscles cautiously after the exercise.

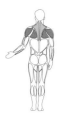

Cable external rotation

MAIN MUSCLES:
infraspinatus muscle, teres minor, deltoid muscle *(Deltoideus)* posterior region *(Pars spinalis)*

SUPPORTING MUSCLES:
rhomboid muscles *(Rhomboidei)*, trapezius muscle *(Trapezius)*, especially middle fibers *(Pars transversa)*

1. Starting position

Sit to one side of the cable machine on a flat bench, and draw the cable upward from below from the opposite side (with the arm on the opposite side of the bench to the cable machine). Bend the arm in the elbow joint at a right angle and rest the elbow slightly away from upper body, resting the forearm on the thigh. The forearm should be parallel to the upper body in the starting position and the hand pointing toward the pulley. The other arm is stretched out and the hand grips the bench for support. Consciously tense the trunk and shoulder muscles.

Exercise variation:

➤ The exercise can also be performed in a standing position using a height adjustable pulley. In this version, spread the upper arm slightly away from the body and support it with a rolled up towel between the arm and body.

Evaluation:

A technically demanding exercise for concentrated training of the important external rotation function of the shoulder joint. The exercise should be performed under professional guidance and checked in a mirror.

Suitability:

Under the conditions specified above the exercise is appropriate for all levels of ability.

COORDINATION DEMANDS:
● ● ● ● ◐

TRAINING EFFECTIVENESS:
● ● ● ● ●

STRESS POTENTIAL:
● ● ● ◐ ○

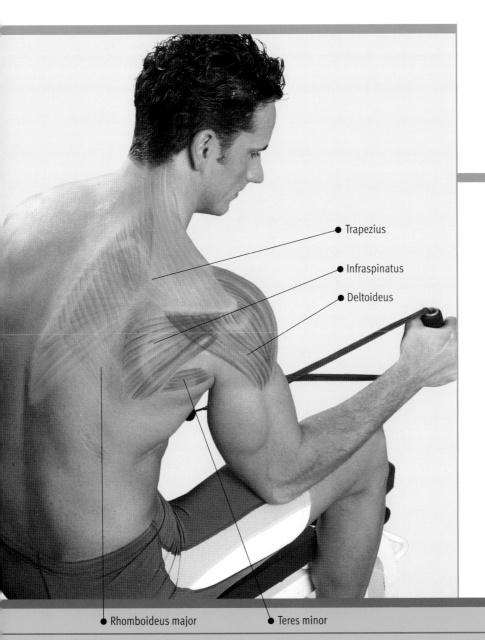

Trapezius

Infraspinatus

Deltoideus

Rhomboideus major

Teres minor

2. Movement

Rotate the handle past the body. The turning movement runs through an imaginary axis between the shoulder and elbow joint. The wrist describes approximately a quarter circle outward. The outward rotation ends when the hand is pointing a little beyond the shoulder axis. Now bring the handle back slowly against the pull of the cable to the starting position with the forearm parallel to the upper body. Change sides and repeat the exercise.

Important tips:

➤ Choose a cable machine with precisely adjustable resistance, and with a height-adjustable pulley if possible.

➤ The entire movement consists of a turning motion in the shoulder joint, with the wrist rotating a quarter circle outward. The shoulder joint should always be stable and relaxed.

COORDINATION DEMANDS:
● ● ● ◐ ○

TRAINING EFFECTIVENESS:
● ● ● ◐ ○

STRESS POTENTIAL:
● ● ● ◐ ○

MAIN MUSCLES:
rhomboid muscles *(Rhomboidei)*, trapezius muscle *(Trapezius)*, especially middle fibers *(Pars transversa)*, deltoid muscle *(Deltoideus)* posterior region *(Pars spinalis)*

SUPPORTING MUSCLES:
teres minor, rotary cuff muscle*(Infraspinatus)*, lower back muscle *(Erector spinae)*, large buttocks muscle *(Gluteus maximus)*

Shoulder raise lying on the stomach

Evaluation:
An effective exercise for the upper back and the rear shoulder area. It requires good stability, in order to avoid strain in the lumbar vertebrae.

Suitability:
Suitable for beginners with good stability.

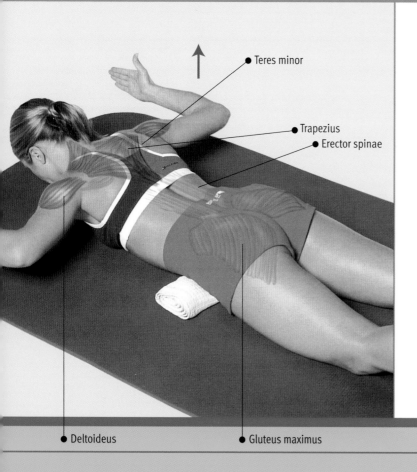

Teres minor

Trapezius

Erector spinae

Deltoideus

Gluteus maximus

Starting position and movement

Lie on the stomach on a mat and support the pelvis with a rolled up towel. Bend the arms upward at your sides next to the body in a U-shape. The backs of the hands should point outward. In order to stabilize the pelvis, tense the buttock muscles and pull in the tips of the toes slightly. Now raise the head, elbows, and hands—in that order—a few inches above the floor and then lift the arms in parallel (in the U-shape) but higher, so that the shoulder blades are brought closer together. Hold this position for a few seconds then return slowly to the starting position.

Exercises variations:
➤ To intensify the exercise the elbows can be lifted even higher.
➤ In addition, the external rotation in the shoulder joint can be emphasized. The hands should then be a little higher than the level of the elbows.

Important tips:
➤ The head remains in a neutral position as an extension of the back, the gaze is directed downward.
➤ Maintain tension in the buttocks and trunk muscles, in order to prevent lapsing into a hollow back.
➤ Ensure your breathing is even and regular.

Biceps, Triceps, and Forearms

Hardly any other muscle is so closely associated with strength training as the biceps. This surface muscle bulges visibly under the skin when contracted. Along with the lower biceps *(Brachialis)* and bracioradialis muscles that are primarily located in the forearm region, the main function of the biceps is to flex the elbow joint. As an articulated muscle, the biceps also affects the shoulder joint. The arm triceps muscle *(Triceps brachii)* lies on the back of the upper arm. Its main function is to extend the elbow joint. In this respect, it is the counterpart to the flexor muscles in the front of the arm. The triceps is especially important in sports, since it is involved in throwing and hitting motions, that require the fast and forceful extension of the elbow joint, known as explosive force.

THE FOREARMS

When the upper arms are trained, the forearms are strengthened at the same time, because dumbbells or handles always have to be held firmly and stabilized. In the first instance, the demand on the lower arm muscles is static. For dynamic strengthening, special exercises for the wrist flexors and extenders are provided on pages 150 and 152.

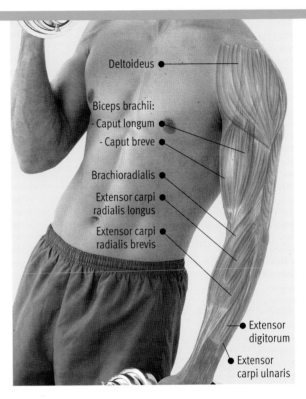

Deltoideus

Biceps brachii:
- Caput longum
- Caput breve

Brachioradialis

Extensor carpi radialis longus

Extensor carpi radialis brevis

Extensor digitorum

Extensor carpi ulnaris

The muscles of the upper and lower arms, viewed from the front and back.

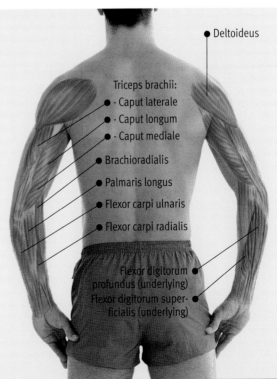

Deltoideus

Triceps brachii:
- Caput laterale
- Caput longum
- Caput mediale

Brachioradialis

Palmaris longus

Flexor carpi ulnaris

Flexor carpi radialis

Flexor digitorum profundus (underlying)

Flexor digitorum superficialis (underlying)

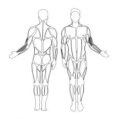

MAIN MUSCLES:
arm biceps *(Biceps brachii)*, lower biceps
(Brachialis), brachioradialis

SUPPORTING MUSCLES:
flexing muscles of the forearm

Lever preacher curl

1. Starting position

Place the upper arms parallel, resting on the padding, so that the elbow joints are an extension of the machine's axis of rotation. Select a stable sitting position with the legs bent at right angles. Tense the trunk muscles to hold this position.

Exercise variation:

➤ Machines equipped with movable handles enable the hand position to be varied. Begin the movement with your hands slightly turned inward and twist the forearms until the palms are pointing to the body (underhand grip or supination).

Evaluation:

An exercise for single joint training (elbow flexing) of the arm flexing muscles.

Suitability:

Because of the simple movement and good machine guidance, the biceps machine is suitable basic training for all levels of ability.

COORDINATION DEMANDS:
● ○ ○ ○ ○

TRAINING EFFECTIVENESS:
● ● ● ◐ ○

STRESS POTENTIAL:
● ● ○ ○ ○

rachioradialis ●————

Brachialis ●————

● Biceps brachii

2. Movement

Hold the machine lever with a steady grip and make sure that the wrists are in a neutral extension of the forearms(do not let them buckle). Bend the arms in a uniform movement, until the elbows are bent at over 90 degrees. Then return to the starting position in a controlled fashion, but not so far as to fully extend the elbows.

Important tips:

➤ The position of the elbow joints remains the same the entire time. The distance of the elbow joints from each other and from the machine axis should not change during the movement.

➤ Always keep the shoulders in a neutral position (do not pull them forward or upward).

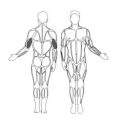

Lever triceps extension

MAIN MUSCLES:
arm triceps muscle *(Triceps brachii)*, the middle and posterior region especially *(Caput mediale* and *laterale)*

SUPPORTING MUSCLES:
flexing muscles of the forearms

1. Starting position

Place the upper arms parallel on the padding, so that the elbow joints are in line with the machine's axis of rotation. Adjust the seat so that the knee joints are bent almost at right angles. Straighten your back and use the padding on the seat back for support. Stabilize the back and the shoulder girdle by tensing the trunk and shoulder muscles. Grip the handles and bend the elbow joints as much as possible.

Evaluation:

A basic exercise for single-joint training of the elbow extension muscles.
The movement is specified by the machine and is therefore easy to perform.

Suitability:

For the above reasons the exercise is also suitable for beginners.

COORDINATION DEMANDS:
● ○ ○ ○ ○

TRAINING EFFECTIVENESS:
● ● ● ◐ ○

STRESS POTENTIAL:
● ● ○ ○ ○

● Triceps brachii   ● Deltoideus

2. Movement

Push the handles away fom you with the edge of your hands until the the elbow joints are extended (but not overextended). Hold this position briefly and then return to the starting position against the resistance of the machine. Always keep the muscles tense.

Important tips:

➤ Avoid jerky movement and acceleration.
➤ Make sure that the elbows stay in the area of the machine pivot point and that the shoulders are in a neutral position throughout the movement (do not pull them up).

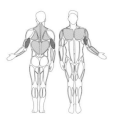

MAIN MUSCLES:
arm triceps muscle *(Triceps brachii)*

SUPPORTING MUSCLES:
large pectoral muscle *(Pectoralis major)*, deltoid
muscle *(Deltoideus)* anterior region *(Pars clavicularis)*, trapezius muscle, especially lower region
(Pars ascendens), latissimus dorsi, holding muscles of the shoulder blades, flexing muscles of
the forearm

Assisted dip

1. Starting position

Position yourself on the tread or
the knee padding (depending on
the machine type), so that the handle grips can be held at the sides of
the body. Stabilize the posture by
actively tensing the trunk muscles
and hold your wrists so that they
are an extension of the forearms
(no bending).

Exercise variation:

➤ Well trained individuals can exercise on machines without support. This intensifies the training
  and the coordination demands are greater because the body must be symmetrically counterbalanced.

Evaluation:

A very effective compound exercise for combined strengthening of the triceps with exercising the chest and shoulder muscles.

Suitability:

Recommended for all training levels. With the assistance of the tread or kneeling surface, beginners can also perform the exercise without problems.

COORDINATION DEMANDS:
● ● ○ ○ ○

TRAINING EFFECTIVENESS:
● ● ● ● ○

STRESS POTENTIAL:
● ● ○ ○ ○

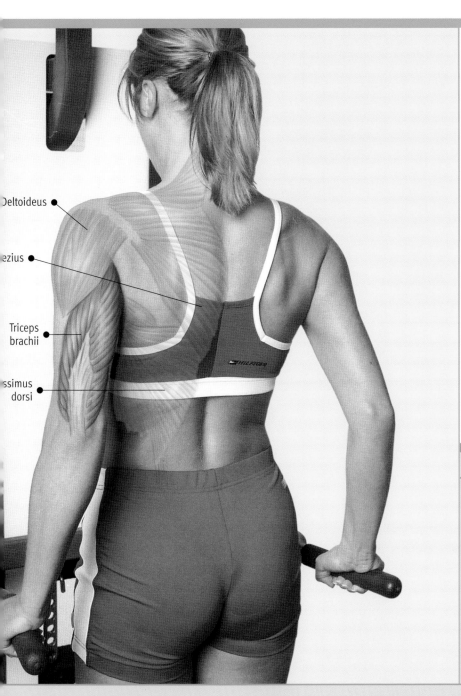

Deltoideus

ezius

Triceps brachii

ssimus dorsi

2. Movement

Press yourself in a uniform movement upward, slightly spreading the elbows and holding them close to the body. At the highest point of the movement, the elbows should be almost (but not completely!) extended, so that the muscle tension is always maintained. Then let down the body slowly and in a controlled manner until the elbows are bent at right angles (the upper arms should be as horizontal as possible, i.e., parallel to the floor).

Important tips:

➤ Make sure your wrists are always stable and vertical and avoid compensatory movements in the spine (no swinging movements).

➤ Letting the trunk sink too much, so that the elbows are above the shoulder level, will overload the shoulder joint.

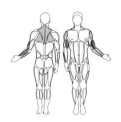

MAIN MUSCLES:
arm biceps muscle (*Biceps brachii*), lower biceps (*Brachialis*), brachiradialis muscle

SUPPORTING MUSCLES:
deltoid muscle (*Deltoideus*) anterior region (*Pars clavicularis*), trapezius muscle, holding muscles of the shoulder blades, flexing muscles of the forearm

Biceps curl with barbell

1. Starting position

Position your legs in a narrow stride, with your knees slightly bent. Stabilize the pelvis and the upper body by actively tensing the trunk muscles. Hold the barbell at about shoulder width and lock the wrists. The arms should be slightly bent. Always keep the shoulders in a neutral position (do not pull them forward or upwards).

Exercise variations:

➤ Use a z-bar, like the one in the picture, if available. The advantage is that the wrists hold the bar in a neutral position and the movement as a whole is smoother.

➤ In order to intensify the exercise, small range repetitions (end contractions) can be performed in the end phase.

Evaluation:

A compound exercise for the entire arm-flexing muscles. As with all exercises performed using free weights, good basic stability and movement technique are absolutely necessary.

Suitability:

For more advanced trainers.

Deltoideus

Biceps brachii

Brachioradialis

2. Movement

Bend the arms in a uniform movement, until the bar is at around shoulder height. Hold the position briefly at the point of reversal and then bring down the barbell slowly. The elbows should still be bent at the lowest point, or the muscle effort will be counteracted.

● Brachialis

Important tips:

➤ Avoid any compensatory movements, especially in the area of the trunk (that might produce a hollow back) and the shoulder girdle. Reduce the weight if necessary.

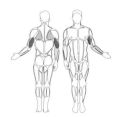

MAIN MUSCLES:
arm triceps muscle *(Triceps brachii)*

SUPPORTING MUSCLES:
holding muscles of the shoulder blade,
flexing muscles of the forearm

Overhead barbell extension

1. Starting position

Sit in a stable position on a flat
bench. Tense the trunk muscles
and straighten the upper body.
Hold the bar—a z-bar, if possible—with a narrow grip and let
the weight drop back, i.e., behind
the head. The upper arms should
be more-or-less horizontal.

Exercise variation:

➤ In order to increase the training stimulation the exercise can be performed while lying on the back.
In that case, place the feet on the bench with the knees bent in order to prevent hollowing the back.
The back of the head should be even with the edge of the padding.
In this variation the arms are extended backward in line with the trunk.

Evaluation:

A basic exercise for the elbow extension muscles. Since the movement takes place out of sight, if possible, it should be controlled with a mirror.

Suitability:

With an appropriate weight the exercise is suitable for beginners.

COORDINATION DEMANDS:
● ● ◐ ○ ○

TRAINING EFFECTIVENESS:
● ● ● ● ○

STRESS POTENTIAL:
● ● ● ○ ○

Triceps brachii

2. Movement

Lift the bar upward using the backs of the upper arm muscles in a uniform movement, until the elbows are fully extended. Then let the bar down slowly and deliberately, until it has returned to the starting position.

Important tips:

➤ Make sure in all triceps exercises that the movement is performed exclusively with the elbows.

➤ Avoid parallel and compensatory movements in the shoulder or in the trunk area.

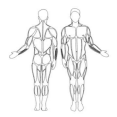

MAIN MUSCLES:
flexor carpi radialis, flexor carpi ulnaris, palmaris longus, flexor digitorum superficialis and profundis

SUPPORTING MUSCLES:
none

Barbell wrist curl

1. Starting position

Sit with your feet at the width of your hips on a bench. The forearms rest parallel on the thighs, and the wrists are free. Grab the bar in a so-called undergrip (the palms point upwards) and let the the weight of the bar pull down the wrists a little. The back is straight and the head is in an extension of the back.

Exercise variations:

➤ You can also support the forearms between the legs on the bench or in a standing position on the support board of a biceps curler.

➤ The one-armed variation with the dumbbell is also very effective. Don't forget to change sides!

Evaluation:

A special exercise for stabilizing the wrists, especially the extension function of the backs of the hands. The exercise is good preparation for training with free weights with a steady grip.

Suitability:

Recommended for all levels.

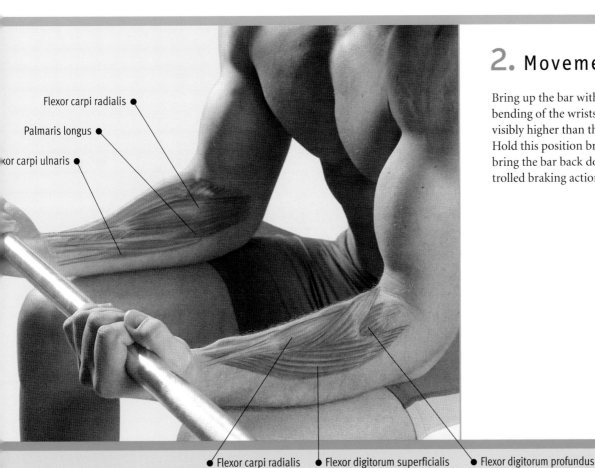

Flexor carpi radialis

Palmaris longus

xor carpi ulnaris

Flexor carpi radialis ● Flexor digitorum superficialis ● Flexor digitorum profundus

2. Movement

Bring up the bar with a uniform bending of the wrists, until it is visibly higher than the forearms. Hold this position briefly, and then bring the bar back down in a controlled braking action.

Important tips:

➤ Start out with a smaller weight and a limited range of movement. To intensify the training, first increase the angle, then the weight.

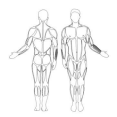

MAIN MUSCLES:
extensor carpi longus and brevis, extensor carpi ulnaris, extensor digitorum

SUPPORTING MUSCLES:
none

Barbell reverse wrist curl

1. Starting position

Sit with your feet at the width of your hips on a bench. The forearms should rest parallel on the thighs, and the wrists free. Grab the bar in a so-called overgrip (with the backs of the hands pointing upward) and let the the weight of the bar pull down your wrists a little. The back should be straight and the head in line with the back.

Exercise variations:

➤ You can also support the forearms between the legs on the bench or in a standing position on the support board of a biceps curler.

➤ The one-armed variation with the dumbbell is also very effective. Don't forget to change sides.

Evaluation:

A special exercise for stabilizing the wrists, especially the extension function along the backs of the hands. The exercise is good preparation for training with free weights, as it builds up strength in the forearms.

Suitability:

Recommended for all levels.

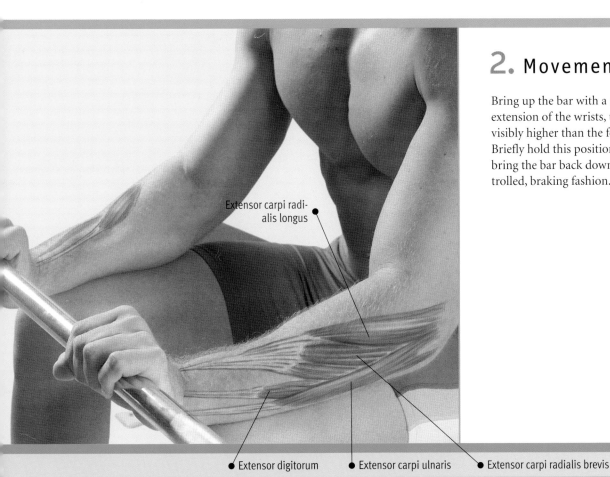

Extensor carpi radi-
alis longus

Extensor digitorum   Extensor carpi ulnaris   Extensor carpi radialis brevis

2. Movement

Bring up the bar with a uniform extension of the wrists, until it is visibly higher than the forearms. Briefly hold this position, and then bring the bar back down in a controlled, braking fashion.

Important tips:

➤ Start out with less weight and a limited range of movement.
In order to intensify the training, first increase the angle, then the weight.

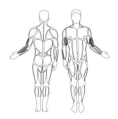

MAIN MUSCLES:
arm biceps *(Biceps brachii)*, lower biceps
(Brachialis), brachioradialis

SUPPORTING MUSCLES:
flexing muscles of the forearm

Concentration curl

1. Starting position

Sit with your legs spread wide
apart on a bench and support
yourself with one hand on your
thigh. Grab the dumbbell with the
other hand and lay the upper arm
on the inner side of the thigh. The
arm is almost outstretched and the
palm is in an extension of the
inner side of the lower arm. Keep
the upper body straight but slightly
forward leaning with the head in
an extension of the back.

Exercise variation:

➤ To enhance the exercise, you can do small repetitions in the last third of the movement
(end contractions).

Evaluation:

A highly effective free weight exercise for strengthening and shaping the biceps.

Suitability:

The concentration curl is intended for more advanced individuals who have already built up the biceps with simpler basic exercises.

COORDINATION DEMANDS:
● ● ● ○ ○

TRAINING EFFECTIVENESS:
● ● ● ● ●

STRESS POTENTIAL:
● ● ● ◐ ○

Biceps brachii ●
Brachioradialis ●

● Brachialis

2. Movement

Bend the elbows slowly and with concentration in a uniform movement. Hold the position briefly in the area of greatest bend and then bring the dumbbell down again to the starting position with the arm slightly bent in a controlled, braking motion. The shoulders and trunk should always be stable. Change sides when you are through.

Important tips:

➤ Ensure the wrists are always held steady and the dumbbell is kept stable in an extension of the forearm (no buckling).

➤ The movement should take place entirely in the elbow joint.

Dumbbell kickback

MAIN MUSCLES:
arm triceps muscle *(Triceps brachii)*,
especially inner region *(Caput longum)*

SUPPORTING MUSCLES:
deltoid muscle *(Deltoideus)* posterior region
(Pars spinalis), latissimus dorsi, teres major,
holding muscles of the shoulder blades

1. Starting position

Support yourself on one side on a
flat bench. The knee and shoulder
of the side that is supported form a
line, the back is straight and firmly
counterbalanced. The foot on the
free side stands firmly on the floor.
Hold the dumbbell near to the
body. Bend the elbow at a right
angle. The upper arm is parallel to
the trunk and the back of the hand
points outward.

Exercise variation:

➤ The basic exercise is performed using a neutral hand position (the back of the hand pointing outward
throughout the movement). Alternatively, the dumbbell can be turned inward (pronation) during the
extension movement. The back of the hand should then point down toward the floor in the end position.

Evaluation:

A favorite dumbbell exercise for one-armed training of the elbow extension muscles. The kickbacks are only effective, however, when the movement technique is exactly right.

Suitability:

Primarily for more advanced individuals.

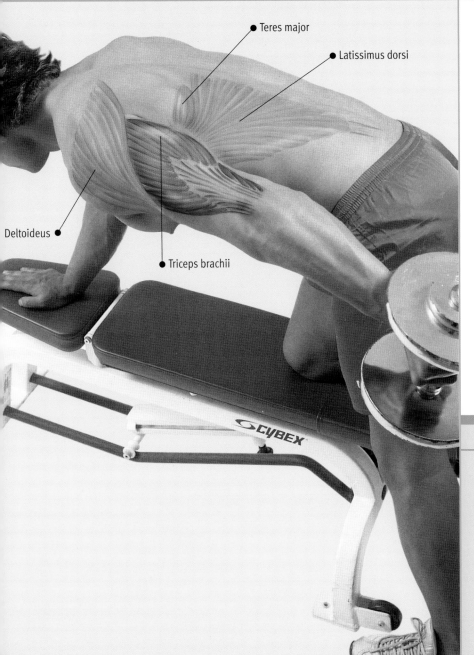

Teres major

Latissimus dorsi

Deltoideus

Triceps brachii

2. Movement

From this position, press the dumbbell backward, until the elbow is extended. The arm should run parallel to the trunk. Hold this position briefly and guide the dumbbell slowly back to the starting position with the elbow joint in a right angle again. Change sides.

Important tips:

➤ Always keep the dumbbell close to the body and avoid spreading the arms, especially at the end of the movement.

➤ Keep the trunk straight (with the head in line with the back) and make sure that both arms are evenly exercised.

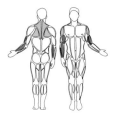

MAIN MUSCLES:
arm biceps muscle *(Biceps brachii)*,
lower biceps *(Brachialis)*, brachioradialis

SUPPORTING MUSCLES:
deltoid muscle *(Deltoideus)* anterior region
(Pars clavicularis), trapezius muscle,
holding muscles of the shoulder blades,
flexing muscles of the forearm

Cable biceps curl

1. Starting position

Attach a biceps bar or two handles
(see photo) to the lower pulley of a
cable machine.
A V-shaped grip position is a good
one. Find a stable starting position
in a short stride stance in front of
the cable pull. The knee should be
slightly bent, the trunk actively
stabilized.

Exercise variation:

➤ You can also perform a one-armed version of the movement. Make sure, in that case, that the shoulder
axis is stable and both sides are trained with the same weight.

Evaluation:

A standard cable exercise for strengthening and shaping the arm-flexing muscles.

Suitability:

Because the movement sequence is quite simple, the exercise can be performed by beginners.

● Brachialis ● Brachioradialis ● Biceps brachii

COORDINATION DEMANDS:
● ● ● ○ ○

TRAINING EFFECTIVENESS:
● ● ● ● ◑

STRESS POTENTIAL:
● ● ● ○ ○

2. Movement

Concentrate and bend the elbows slowly in a uniform movement. Hold the position briefly at the point of maximum flex and guide the handles or bar back to the starting position, against the resistance of the weight. The elbows should now be slightly bent. Keep the shoulders parallel in a neutral position. The trunk should always be stable.

Important tips:

➤ Make sure the wrists are always steady and that the handles or the bar are always firmly guided in line with the forearm (no buckling).

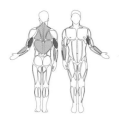

Cable pushdown

MAIN MUSCLES:
arm triceps muscle *(Triceps brachii)*, especially posterior and middle region *(Caput laterale and mediale)*

SUPPORTING MUSCLES:
trapezius muscle posterior region *(Pars spinalis)*, latissimus dorsi, teres major, holding muscles of the shoulder blades, flexing muscles of the forearm

1. Starting position

Attach a V-shaped grip (see photo) or a triceps rope to the lower pulley of a cable machine. Find a stable starting position in a short stride stance in front of the cable pull. Bend the knees slightly and keep the back straight.
Pull the handle (or the rope) straight down, until the elbows are bent at an angle of just over 90 degrees. Hold the upper arms tightly to the sides. Hold the handle with the wrists in a stable extension of the forearm, with the backs of the hands pointing in a V-shape upward and outward.

Exercise variations:

➤ Using a conventional handle, the exercise can be performed one-armed. In this version, ensure symmetrical stability of the shoulder. The arm that is not being trained is used to support the movement on the cable machine.

➤ You can gradually turn the handle inward (pronation)during the extension movement, so that the thumb side does not point toward the body but it, and the arm, are further back (retroversion). In this position the inner triceps region *(Caput longum)* is activated.

Evaluation:

A simple, but intensive cable pull exercise for the elbow extender.

Suitability:

With weights adjusted for the individual, the cable pushdown is suitable for all levels.

COORDINATION DEMANDS:
● ● ◑ ○ ○

TRAINING EFFECTIVENESS:
● ● ● ● ◑

STRESS POTENTIAL:
● ● ○ ○ ○

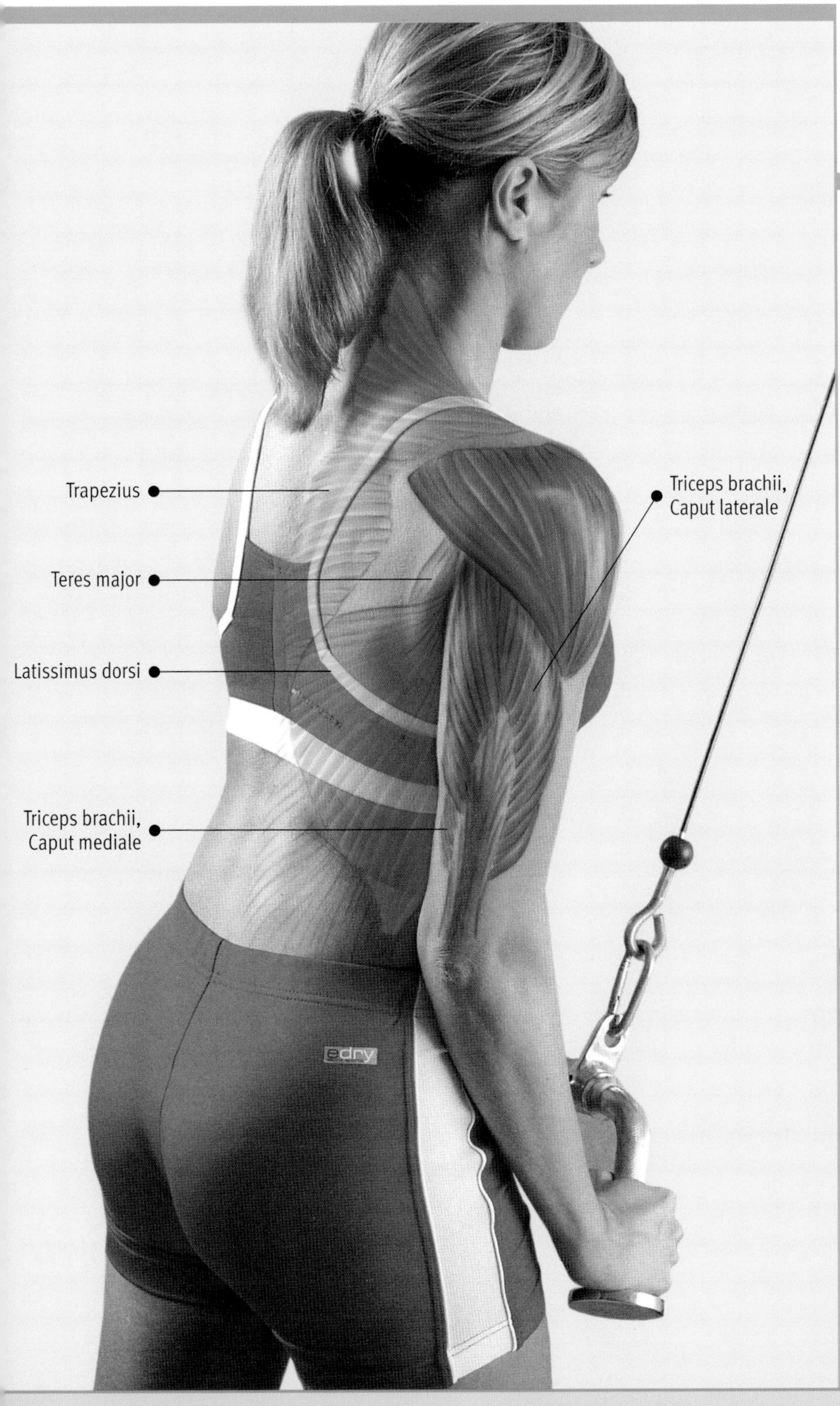

Trapezius ●

Teres major ●

Latissimus dorsi ●

Triceps brachii, Caput mediale ●

Triceps brachii, Caput laterale ●

2. Movement

Push the handle toward the body from this position, until the elbow joints are extended. Hold the position briefly and guide the movement, against the resistance of the weights, back to the starting position.

Important tips:

➤ Ensure the arms describe a linear movement without compensatory movement in the elbow joint.

COORDINATION DEMANDS:
● ● ● ◐ ○

TRAINING EFFECTIVENESS:
● ● ● ◐ ○

STRESS POTENTIAL:
● ● ● ● ○

MAIN MUSCLES:
arm triceps muscle *(Triceps brachii)*

SUPPORTING MUSCLES:
large pectoral muscle *(Pectoralis major)*,
especially lower region *(Pars abdominalis)*,
deltoid muscle *(Deltoideus)* anterior region
(Pars clavicularis), holding muscles of the
shoulder blades

Dips with stool

Evaluation:

An intensive complex exercise using the weight of the body. The
exercise must be performed in a controlled fashion, in order to
avoid overloading the shoulder region.

Suitability:

Primarily for individuals with greater training experience.

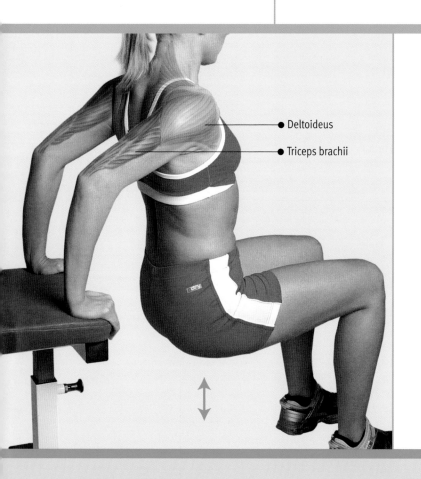

● Deltoideus
● Triceps brachii

Starting position and Movement

Support yourself with your hands parallel
and side-by-side behind your back, gripping
the edge of the padding of a stable stool or
training bench. Place the feet far enough
away from the body so that the buttocks are
about a shoe-length from the stool or bench.
Now slowly lower the upper body, leading
with the buttocks, gradually increasing the
flex of the arms in the direction of the floor.
The downward movement ends when the
the elbows are at a right angle. Now push the
body back up to the starting position, without swinging. The elbows should remain
slightly bent (not overextended).

Exercise variation:

➤ The intensity can be varied by changing the distance of
the trunk from the stool or bench. The further the distance,
the more difficult the exercise will be. The load on the shoulder joint also increases.

Important tips:

➤ Do not drop down too low or the
shoulder joint will become overextended.

Index

Subject index

Exercise index

Important notice

The author and publisher have made every effort to ensure the information provided in this book conforms to national health and fitness standards and that the exercises are suitable for healthy individuals. It is not meant to replace the advice of a physician. Each reader is asked to make a personal decision as to which exercises are appropriate and how closely they want to follow the advice in this book. Neither the author nor publisher can assume responsibility for any injury, loss or harm resulting from the practices offered in this book.

Muscle Training
for some of the most popular sports

	Recommended strength training
Badminton	Whole body training to improve performance. Symmetrical strengthening of all muscles from trunk to upp body to balance out one-sided hitting movements.
Basketball	Targeted leg muscle training for more jumping power. Strengthening of trunk, shoulder, and arm muscles for powerful throwing and one-on-one confrontations.
Cycling	Better performance from targeted strengthening of the legs. Vitally important: Balance training using the abdominal muscles and exercises for straightening the upper body (back and rear shoulder muscles).
Jogging/running/ walking	Muscle training especially for balance: Trunk muscle exercises, in order to prevent back problems, plus chest, shoulder, and arm training for even and uniform body-building.
Soccer and football	Strength training of the leg muscles enhances shooting and jumping power; the strengthening the trunk, shoulders, and arms gives an advantage in one-on-ones, headers, and throwing.
Golf	Balancing out of the one-sided loading of the trunk and shoulder areas resulting from the golf swing: especially abdominal and back muscle exercises as well as strengthening of the chest, shoulder, and arm muscles.
Handball	Strengthening program for the whole body. Regular strength training enhances the throwing and jumping power and improves the physical requirements for one-on-one confrontations.
Inline Skating	Strengthening of the thigh extensors, hip and buttocks muscles for more "pushing" power (pushing off with the skates). Back and abdominal muscle exercises relieve the small of the back, and exercises for the upper body ensure harmonic body building.
Swimming	Muscle training increases performance here. Pulling movements are especially good for upper body traini Depending on the swimming discipline, it is possible to exercise muscles individually.
Downhill skiing	A strengthening of the front thigh muscles enhances performance, especially in steep descents, while tru muscle exercises stabilize and protect the back; strengthening the upper body balances out the primarily overloaded leg muscles.
Cross-country skiing	Strength training improves the skating technique (building up the hip muscles) and the pole work (multi-jointed triceps exercises, such as kickbacks).
Snowboarding	Balance improvement is recommended to counteract the one-sided exertion of the back. Strengthening the thighs improves performance.
Tennis	Uniform strengthening of the trunk, shoulder, and arm muscles. Training of the leg extensors as well as th triceps muscles to improve the serve.
Volleyball	Training for the jumping power is key (leg presses are especially useful). For more ball hitting power: Trunk muscle training together with chest and triceps exercises.
Windsurfing	Targeted buildup of the back, shoulder, and arm muscles. Abdominal muscle exercises stabilize the trunk, while leg muscle exercises improve the surfing performance with foot strap technique.

You can increase your performance in every type of sport with targeted strength training. On the one hand, supplementary muscle training can be targeted for muscles on which particular demands are made in the particular sport; these muscles can then be systematically trained to improve the sport specific performance. On the other hand it is important, especially from the standpoint of general health, to train evenly and regularly and to balance out one-sided exertion; this is especially true for trunk and shoulder girdle muscles, in order to avoid straining the back and the joints.

Improvement of the sport-specific performance: ● ● highly recommended ● recommended
Balancing out one-sided exertion: ○ ○ highly recommended ○ recommended

Legs	Hips/Buttocks	Abdomen	Back	Chest	Shoulder	Arms
● ●	● ●	● ● ○ ○	● ● ○ ○	● ● ○ ○	● ● ○ ○	● ● ○ ○
● ●	● ●	● ●	● ●	● ●	● ●	● ●
● ●	●		○ ○	○	○ ○	○
●	●		○ ○	○	○	
● ●	● ●	● ●	● ● ○	● ● ○	● ● ○	● ● ○
●	●	● ● ○ ○	● ● ● ○	● ● ○	● ● ○ ○	● ● ○
● ●	● ●	● ●	● ●	● ●	● ●	● ●
● ●	● ●	○ ○	● ● ○ ○	○	○	○
● ●	● ●	● ●	● ●	● ●	● ●	● ●
● ●	● ●	○ ○	○ ○	○	○	○
● ●	● ●	● ●	● ●	● ●	● ●	● ●
● ●	● ●	○ ○	● ● ● ○	○	○	
● ●	● ●	● ● ○ ○	● ● ● ○	● ● ○ ○	● ● ○ ○	● ● ○ ○
● ●	● ●	● ● ○ ○	● ● ● ○	● ●	● ● ○ ○	● ●
● ●	● ●	● ● ○ ○	● ● ○ ○	● ●	● ●	● ●

This edition published by:
Barnes & Noble, Inc.,
by arrangement with
GRÄFE UND UNZER VERLAG GmbH,
Munich

© 2003 GRÄFE UND UNZER VERLAG
GmbH, Munich.

Production:
bookwise Medienproduktion GmbH,
Munich

Translation:
Geoffrey Steinherz, Wiesbaden

©2004 Barnes & Noble Books

M 10 9 8 7 6 5 4 3 2

ISBN 0-7607-5463-2

Printed in Slovenia

The author
Elmar Trunz-Carlisi is a sports scientist and the director of the Institute for Prevention and Aftercare in Cologne. As a fitness and health sports training professional, he has published countless articles in popular and professional magazines and books, and has appeared on television. Elmar is a consultant and editor of the German professional fitness magazine *Bodylife* and has been a member of the team of experts for the *Fit for Fun* magazine since 1996.

Dedication
To my wife, Angela and my children, Chiara and Ramon.

The author wishes to thank all those who were involved in the creation of this book. Special thanks are due to Stefan Enders (photos), Dirk Rose (photo assistance), Luitgard Kellner (illustrations), and Monika Rolle (editorial).

Photo production:
Stefan Enders, Cologne

Thanks for your support of the photo production:
– Aggua Sportsclub Team, Troisdorf, for the location
– Cardiofitness GbR, Cologne, for the rental of training equipment

Other photos:
Corbis: page 23. **GU:** pages 2, 6–7, 15 above, 18, 19, 29 re., 39, 55, 73, 91, 107, 119, 139 (Ch. Dahl); back cover, page 3 above, 29 left, 32, 33 left/middle, 35 (E. Geneletti); page 9, 11 left, 12, 26 (A. Hosch); page 27, 31, 33 re., 34, 36-37 (R. Simoni); page 15 bottom (M. Wagenhan). **Jump:** rear cover left, page 11 right **Picture Press:** front cover **Zefa:** page 4.